CW00392827

O Praise God

40 Choral Classics
Compiled by Neil Jenkins

Kevin
Mayhew

13.99

We hope you enjoy the music in this book. Further copies are available from your local music shop or Christian bookshop.

In case of difficulty, please contact the publisher direct by writing to:

The Sales Department
KEVIN MAYHEW LTD
Rattlesden
Bury St Edmunds
Suffolk
IP30 0SZ

Phone 0449 737978
Fax 0449 737834

Please ask for our complete catalogue of outstanding Church Music.

In memory of my mother and father.

First published in Great Britain in 1994 by Kevin Mayhew Ltd

© Copyright 1994 Kevin Mayhew Ltd

ISBN 0 86209 539 5
Catalogue No: 1450020

The texts and music in this book are protected by copyright and may not be reproduced in any way for sale or private use without the consent of the copyright owner.

Front Cover: *Detail from the Ghent Altarpiece* by Jan van Eyck (*c.*1390-1441).
Reproduced by courtesy of the Cathedral of St Bavo, Ghent/
Giraudon/Bridgeman Art Library, London.
Cover design by Juliette Clarke and Graham Johnstone.
Picture Research: Jane Rayson

Music Editors: Anthea Smith and Donald Thomson
Music setting by Chris Hinkins

Printed and bound in Great Britain

Contents

		Page
A Short Requiem	Henry Walford Davies	205
Agnus Dei	Wolfgang Amadeus Mozart	36
And then shall come the glorious morn	Joseph Haydn	97
Ave Maria	Charles Gounod	198
Ave verum corpus	Edward Elgar	122
Ave verum corpus	Wolfgang Amadeus Mozart	216
Blessed are the pure in heart	Henry Walford Davies	160
Bridegroom and Bride	Arthur Sullivan	54
Brother James's Air	Gordon Jacob	12
Cast thy burden upon the Lord	Felix Mendelssohn	52
Come, Holy Ghost	Thomas Attwood	60
Contakion of the Faithful Departed	Traditional Kiev	228
God be in my head (4-part)	Henry Walford Davies	58
God be in my head (6-part)	Henry Walford Davies	59
I will lift up mine eyes	Christopher Brown	80
Jerusalem	Hubert Parry	23
Jesu, joy of man's desiring	Johann Sebastian Bach	248
Laudate Dominum	Wolfgang Amadeus Mozart	240
Lead me, Lord	Samuel Sebastian Wesley	110
Let their celestial concerts all unite	George Frideric Handel	162
Lift thine eyes	Felix Mendelssohn	94
Lo, thus shall the man be blessed	George Frideric Handel	16
Love one another	Samuel Sebastian Wesley	7
Morning has broken	Traditional Gaelic	96
My friend is mine	Johann Sebastian Bach	222
Nunc Dimittis	Christopher Brown	47

		Page
O for the wings of a dove	Felix Mendelssohn	230
O lovely peace	George Frideric Handel	112
O praise God in his holiness	Charles Stanford	220
O worship the King	Wolfgang Amadeus Mozart	174
Panis Angelicus (2-part)	César Franck	65
Panis Angelicus (4-part)	César Franck	70
Since by man came death	George Frideric Handel	33
The Burial Service	William Croft	83
The Lord is my shepherd (SA)	Franz Schubert	140
The Lord is my shepherd (SSAA)	Franz Schubert	150
The Lord is my shepherd (SATB)	Franz Schubert	125
The Lord's my shepherd (Crimond)	Jessie Irvine	215
The Lord's Prayer	Michael Head	118
The Lost Chord	Arthur Sullivan	26
The souls of the righteous	Henry Walford Davies	254
They shall be as happy (3-part)	Henry Purcell	260
They shall be as happy (4-part)	Henry Purcell	257
Three Funeral Sentences	Henry Purcell	181
To thee, O Lord, I yield my spirit	Felix Mendelssohn	78

Foreword

Although it was my original intention to produce separate volumes of choral music for weddings and funerals, so many of the items were common to both books that it was decided to combine them under the title *O Praise God*. Consequently, all the standard favourites can now be found under one cover: *Jesu, joy of man's desiring, Ave verum corpus, God be in my head, Jerusalem* and so forth. The pieces appear in as many different versions as possible. Therefore, the 23rd Psalm will be found in the two-part version to the tune of *Brother James's Air*, in a four-part arrangement to the tune of *Crimond*, and in no less than three different versions of Schubert's fine setting. Several items appear in alternative versions sanctioned by the composers themselves. Purcell's *They shall be as Happy* (from *The Fairy Queen*) is included in Purcell's own SAB and SATB versions. Christopher Brown's *Nunc Dimittis* was written as an SAT piece, but has had a bass part added for this volume and may be performed either way; whilst Michael Head's effective setting of *The Lord's Prayer* is designated as either SATB or Solo (Unison).

For variety, I have included the wedding music from several operatic works. I was delighted to find how well the text of the well-known hymn *O Worship the King* fitted Mozart's music from Act 3 of *The Marriage of Figaro*. Sir Arthur Sullivan's *Bridegroom and Bride* has been given a second verse, although the words are still from the pen of W S Gilbert. Other pieces suitable for weddings, but belonging to larger works, are often difficult to perform satisfactorily without a certain amount of emendation. I have therefore made separate versions of *Love one another* from Wesley's *Blessed be the God and Father* and *O for the wings of a dove* from Mendelssohn's *Hear my prayer* which should prove more practical in this respect. Some traditional solo songs also appear here, but with choral accompaniments, such as the Bach/Gounod *Ave Maria* and Sullivan's *Lost Chord*.

In addition this volume includes settings, in newly-revised editions, of the Purcell *Funeral Sentences* and Croft's *Burial Service*. A Short *Requiem* by Walford Davies, containing brief movements which may be performed separately, completes what I hope will be a volume of lasting, practical worth for choirs of all sizes.

Finally, I should like to acknowledge the assistance given me by Charles Macdonald in preparing the organ accompaniments for this volume.

NEIL JENKINS

LOVE ONE ANOTHER

Text: 1 Peter 1

Music: Samuel Sebastian Wesley (1810-1876) arranged by Neil Jenkins

© Copyright 1994 by Kevin Mayhew Ltd.

It is illegal to photocopy music.

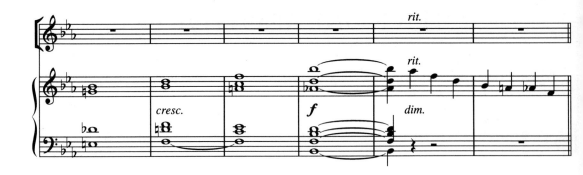

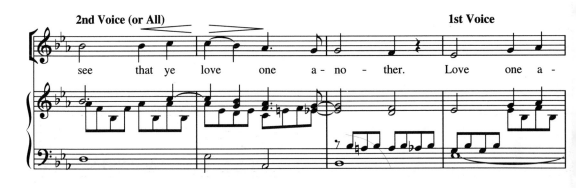

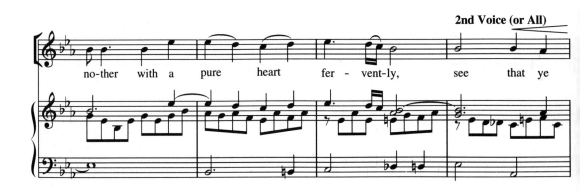

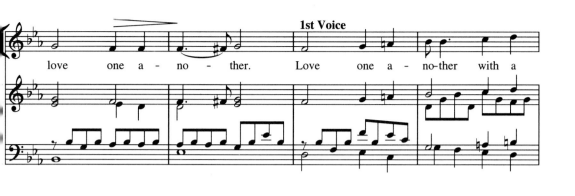

love one a - no - ther. Love one a - no-ther with a

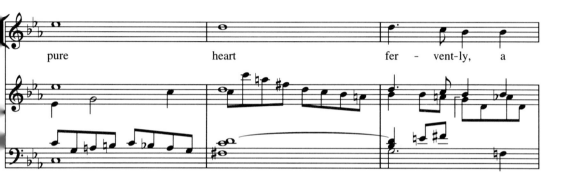

pure heart fer - vent-ly, a

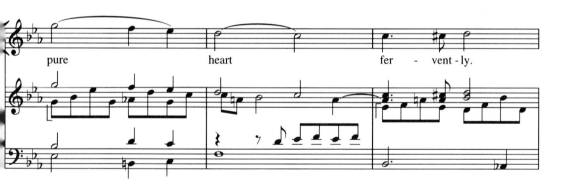

pure heart fer - vent - ly.

See that ye love one a - no - ther. See that ye

love, that ye love one a - no - ther with a pure

2nd Voice (or All)

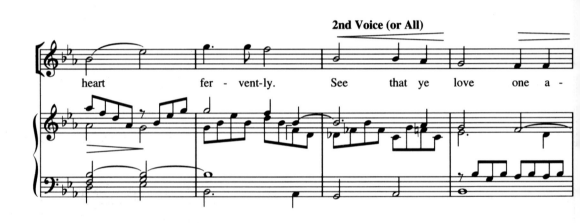

heart fer - vent-ly. See that ye love one a -

1st Voice

with a pure heart, a

2nd Voice (or All)

no - ther with a pure heart, a

pure   heart   fer - vent-ly,   with a   pure

pure   heart   fer - vent-ly,   with a   pure

heart,   a   pure   heart   fer - vent- ly.

heart,   a   pure   heart   fer - vent-ly.

cresc.

rit.

f   *dim.*

Man.   Ped.

11

BROTHER JAMES'S AIR

Text: Psalm 23 from the *Scottish Psalter* (1650)
Music: James Leith MacBeth Bain (*c.*1860-1925)
arranged by Gordon Jacob (1895-1984)

© Copyright 1934 Oxford University Press. Reproduced by permission.
It is illegal to photocopy music.

by.　2. My　soul he doth re - store a-gain and　me to walk doth

molto legato

make　with - in the paths　of　right-eous-ness, e'en　for his own name's

sake,　with - in the paths　of　right-eous-ness, e'en　for his own name's

Descant

3. Yea,　though I walk　in　death's dark vale　yet　will I fear no

All other voices

sake.　3. Yea,　though I walk　in　death's dark vale　yet　will I fear no

13

ill; for thou art with me, and thy rod and staff me com - fort

ill; for thou art with me, and thy rod and staff me com-fort

mf

still, thy rod and staff me com - fort

mf

still, thy rod and staff me com-fort still, me com - fort

mf (2nd time f)

still. 4. My ta - ble thou hast fur - nish - ed in
5. Good - ness and mer - cy all my life shall

mf (2nd time f)

still. 4. My ta - ble thou hast fur - nish - ed in
5. Good - ness and mer - cy all my life shall

mf (2nd time f)

Ped.

14

LO, THUS SHALL THE MAN BE BLESSED

Text: Psalm 128: 5

Music: George Frideric Handel (1685-1759) arranged by Paul Steinitz

© Copyright 1971 Oxford University Press. Reproduced by permission.

It is illegal to photocopy music.

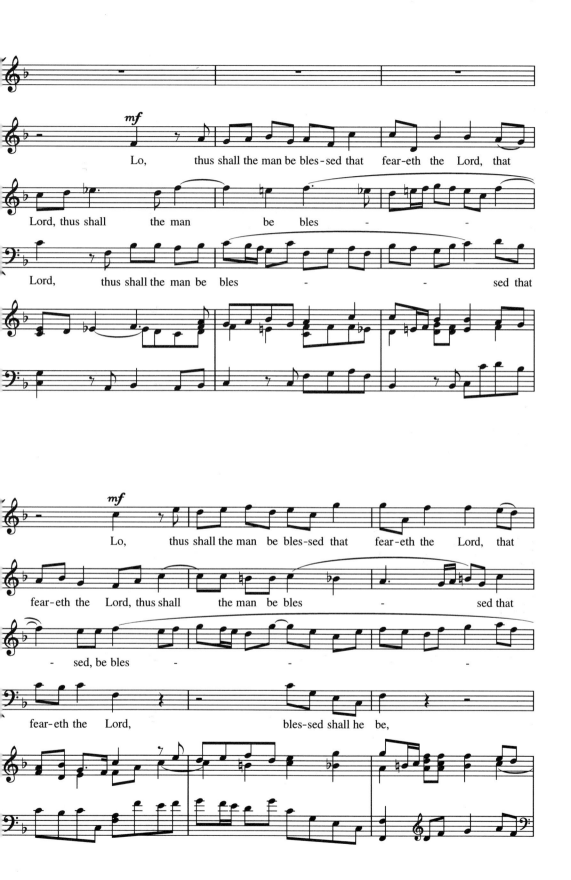

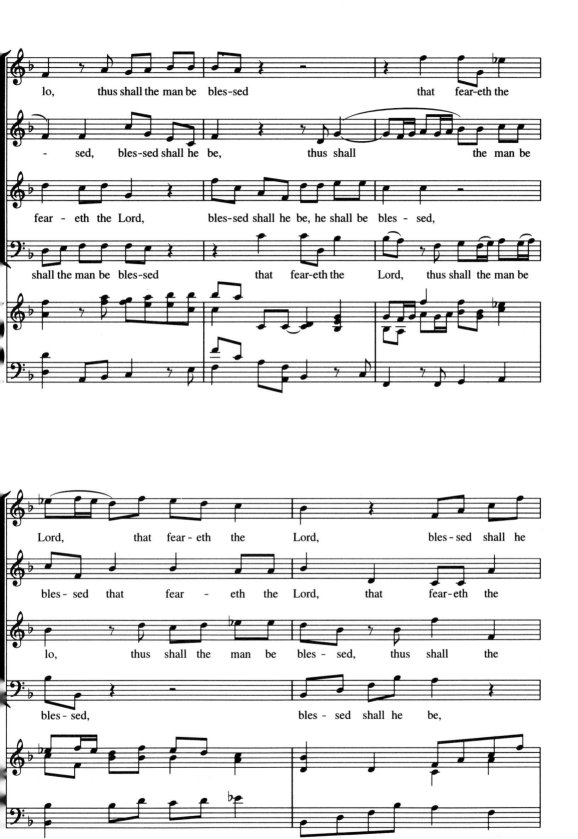

19

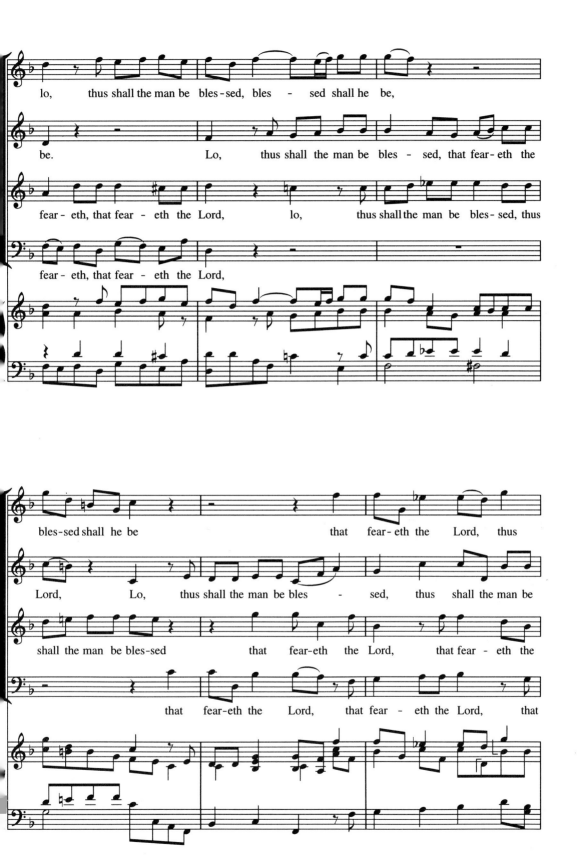

lo, thus shall the man be bles-sed, bles - sed shall he be,

be. Lo, thus shall the man be bles - sed, that fear-eth the

fear - eth, that fear - eth the Lord, lo, thus shall the man be bles- sed, thus

fear - eth, that fear - eth the Lord,

bles-sed shall he be that fear-eth the Lord, thus

Lord, Lo, thus shall the man be bles - sed, thus shall the man be

shall the man be bles-sed that fear-eth the Lord, that fear - eth the

that fear-eth the Lord, that fear - eth the Lord, that

shall the man be bles - sed that fear - eth the

bles - sed, thus shall the man be bles - sed

Lord, that fear - eth the Lord, thus

fear - eth the Lord, lo, thus shall the man be

Lord, thus shall the man be bles - sed that fear - eth the Lord.

that fear - eth the Lord, that fear - eth the Lord.

shall the man be bles - sed that fear - eth the Lord.

bles - sed that fear - eth the Lord, that fear - eth the Lord.

JERUSALEM

Text: William Blake (1757-1827)
Music: Hubert Parry (1848-1918)

© Copyright 1994 by Kevin Mayhew Ltd.
It is illegal to photocopy music.

plea-sant pas - tures seen? And did the coun - te-nance di - vine shine forth up-

on our cloud-ed hills? And was Je - ru - sa-lem build - ed here a-mong those

dark sa - ta - nic mills?

Bring me my bow of burn - ing gold! Bring me my

ar - rows of de - sire! Bring me my spear! O clouds un - fold! Bring me my

cha - ri-ot of fire! I will not cease from men - tal fight, nor shall my

sword sleep in my hand, till we have built Je - ru - sa - lem in Eng-land's

green and plea - sant land.

THE LOST CHORD

Text: Adelaide Proctor (1825-1864)
Music: Arthur Sullivan (1842-1900) arranged by Neil Jenkins

© Copyright 1994 by Kevin Mayhew Ltd.
It is illegal to photocopy music.

what I was dream-ing then, but I struck one chord of mu-sic, like the

p

Man.

sound of a great A - men,

f

poco rall.

like the sound of a great A -

f

f

poco rall.

Ped.

p

It

men.

p

Solo: flood-ed the crim-son twi-light, like the close of an an - gel's psalm, and it

S: (hum) *p*
A: (hum) *p*
T: (hum) *p*
B: (hum) *p*

(optional)

Man.

lay on my fe - vered spi - rit, with a touch of in - fi - nite calm. It

such calm. (hum)
such calm. (hum)
such calm. (hum)
such calm. (hum)

Ped.

29

may be that death's bright an-gel will speak in that chord a - gain: it

A - men,

may be that on-ly in heav'n I shall hear that grand A - men, it

A - men,

may be that death's bright an - gel will speak in that chord a -

gain, it may be that on - ly in heav'n I shall hear that
A - men, it may be that on - ly in heav'n I shall hear that

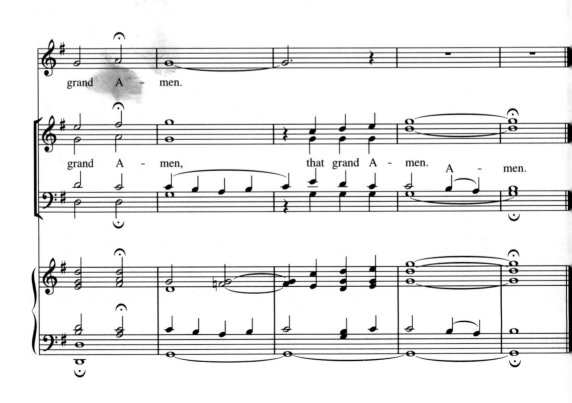

grand A - men.
grand A - men, that grand A - men. A - men.

SINCE BY MAN CAME DEATH

Text: 1 Corinthians 15: 21, 22
Music: George Frideric Handel (1685-1759)

© Copyright 1994 by Kevin Mayhew Ltd.
It is illegal to photocopy music.

live, e - ven so in Christ shall all, so in Christ shall

shall all

all be made a - live, ev'n so in Christ shall all, shall all be made a -

be made a - live,

live.

35

AGNUS DEI

Latin Text: from *The Roman Missal*
English Text: Neil Jenkins
Music: Wolfgang Amadeus Mozart (1756-1791)

A - gnus De - i, a - gnus De - i, qui
Je - sus, Lamb of God, Je - sus, Lamb of God, that

tol - lis pec - ca - ta, pec - ca - ta mun - di, mi - se -
tak - est a - way the sins of the world, have great

© Copyright 1994 by Kevin Mayhew Ltd.
It is illegal to photocopy music.

re - re, mi - se - re - - re no - bis, mi - se -
mer - cy, *have great mer* - - *cy on us, have great*

re - re, mi - se - re - re no - bis.
mer - cy, *have great mer* - *cy on us.*

cresc.

f *p*

A - gnus De - i, a - gnus De - i, qui
Je - *sus, Lamb of God, Je* - *sus, Lamb of God, that*

Gt.

tol - - lis pec - ca - ta, pec - ca - ta mun - di, mi - se -
tak - - *est a - way the sins of the world, have great*

Sw.

37

ca - ta, *way* pec - ca - ta mun - *the sins of the*

di, *world,* a - gnus De - i, *have great mer - cy* qui tol - lis *up - on us,* pec - ca - ta, *O Lamb of God,*

Gt.

Sw.

Andante con moto

do - *grant* na *us* no - *e* - bis *ver - last* pa - *ing* cem, *peace,*

Gt.

do - *grant* na *us* no - *e* - bis *ver - last* pa - *ing* cem, *peace,*

Sw.

Gt.

tr

Man.

Ped.

cem, do — na no — bis pa — cem,
peace, grant us e - ver - last - ing peace,

pa — cem, do — na,
e - ver - last - ing peace, grant us,

do — na no — bis pa — cem, do — na
grant us e - ver - last - ing peace, grant us,

do — na no — bis pa — cem, do — na,
grant us e - ver - last - ing peace, grant us,

Ped.

do — na no — bis pa — cem.
grant us e - ver - last - ing peace.

do — na no — bis pa — cem.
grant us e - ver - last - ing peace.

do — na no — bis pa — cem.
grant us e - ver - last - ing peace.

do — na no — bis pa — cem.
grant us e - ver - last - ing peace.

42

43

cem,   do - na,   do - na, do - na
peace,   grant   us   thy   peace, grant us

Man.   Ped.

no - bis pa - cem,   do - na no - bis pa -
e - ver - last - ing peace,   grant us e - ver - last - ing

cem,   do - na no - bis pa - cem,   do - na no - bis pa - cem.
peace,   grant us, grant us thy   peace,   grant us, grant us thy   peace.

46

NUNC DIMITTIS

Text: Luke 2: 29-32
Music: Christopher Brown (*b.*1943)

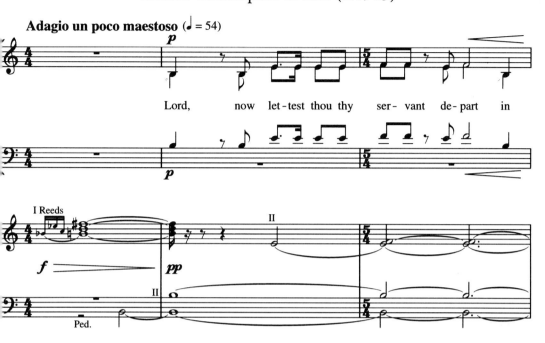

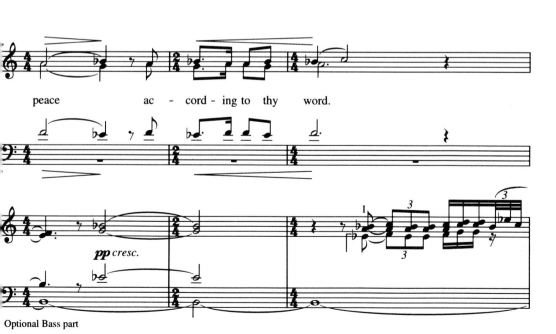

Optional Bass part

© Copyright 1994 by Kevin Mayhew Ltd.
It is illegal to photocopy music.

For mine eyes have seen thy sal - va - tion, which thou hast pre-

pared be - fore the face of all peo - ple;

to be a light to light-en the gen - tiles, and to be the

glo - ry of thy peo-ple Is - - - ra - el.

Glo - ry be to the Fa - ther, and to the

Glo - ry be to the Fa - ther, and to the

Glo - ry be to the Fa - ther, and to the

Glo - ry be to the Fa - ther, and to the

Son, and to the Ho - ly Ghost; as it was in the be - gin-ning, is now and e-ver

Son, and to the Ho - ly Ghost; as it was in the be - gin-ning, is now and e-ver

Son, and to the Ho - ly Ghost; as it was in the be - gin-ning, is now and e-ver

Son, and to the Ho - ly Ghost; as it was in the be - gin-ning, is now and e-ver

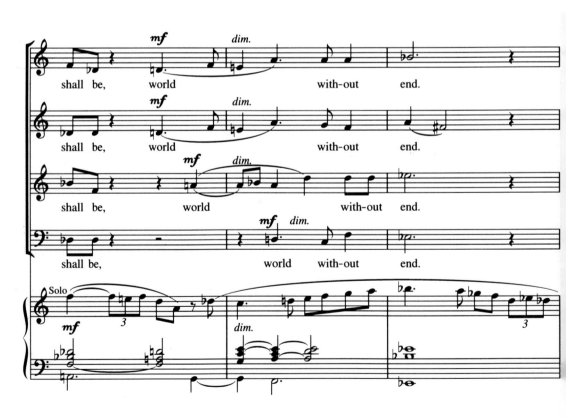

shall be, world with-out end.

shall be, world with-out end.

shall be, world with-out end.

shall be, world with-out end.

CAST THY BURDEN UPON THE LORD

Text: from Psalms 16, 25, 55, 108
Music: Felix Mendelssohn (1809-1847)

© Copyright 1994 by Kevin Mayhew Ltd.
It is illegal to photocopy music.

right hand. Thy mer - cy, Lord, is great, and far a - bove the heav'ns. Let none be made a - sham - ed, that wait up - on thee!

BRIDEGROOM AND BRIDE

Text: William Schwenk Gilbert (1836-1911) adapted by Neil Jenkins
Music: Arthur Sullivan (1842-1900)

© Copyright 1994 by Kevin Mayhew Ltd.
It is illegal to photocopy music.

bride! Knot that's in - so - lu - ble, voi- ces all vo - lu-ble hail it with pride.

bride! Ah,

Bride - groom and bride! We in sin - ce - ri - ty, wish you pros- pe - ri - ty,

Bride - groom and bride! Ah,

bride- groom and bride! We in sin - ce - ri - ty, wish you pros-

We in sin - ce - ri - ty, wish you pros-

pe - ri - ty, bride-groom and bride, bride - groom and bride!

pe - ri - ty, bride-groom and bride, bride - groom and bride!

Bride-groom and bride! In fair phra - ses hymn their prai - ses,

Bride-groom and bride! Ah,

hymn it with pride. Bride - groom and bride! Let them be full of joy,

Bride - groom and bride! Ah,

may their love ne-ver cloy, bride-groom and bride! Let them be full of joy,

Let them be full of joy,

may their love ne - ver cloy, bride - groom and bride! bride -

may their love ne - ver cloy, bride - groom and bride! bride -

groom and bride!

groom and bride!

GOD BE IN MY HEAD (4-part)

Text: from the *Sarum Primer* (1514)
Music: Henry Walford Davies (1869-1941)

© Copyright 1994 by Kevin Mayhew Ltd.
It is illegal to photocopy music.

GOD BE IN MY HEAD (6-part)

Text: from the *Sarum Primer* (1514)
Music: Henry Walford Davies (1869-1941)

© Copyright 1994 by Kevin Mayhew Ltd.
It is illegal to photocopy music.

COME, HOLY GHOST

Text: John Cosin (1594-1672)
Music: Thomas Attwood (1765-1838)

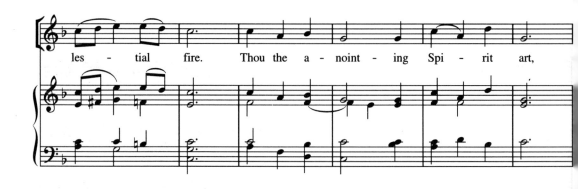

© Copyright 1994 by Kevin Mayhew Ltd.
It is illegal to photocopy music.

from a - bove, is com - fort, life, and fire of love, is

com - fort, life, and fire of love.

Man.

En - a - ble with per - pe - tual light, the

dull - ness of our blind - ed sight; a - noint and cheer our

61

soil - ed face, with the a - bun - dance of thy grace.

Keep far our foes, give peace at home, where thou art guide, no

ill can come; where thou art guide, no ill can come.

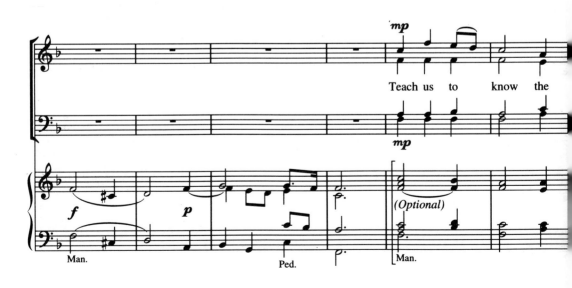

Teach us to know the

(Optional)

Man.   Ped.   Man.

62

Fa - ther, Son, and thee of both to be but one, that

through the a - ges all a - long, this may be our

end - less song: praise to thy e - ter - nal me - rit,

Fa - ther, Son, and Ho - ly Spi - rit, Fa - ther, Son, and

Ho - ly Spi - rit.

Sw. *mf*

dim.

pp

PANIS ANGELICUS (2-part)

Latin Text: Thomas Aquinas (1227-1274)
English Text: Charles Wesley (1707-1788) adapted by Neil Jenkins
Music: César Franck (1822-1890) arranged by Neil Jenkins

Pa - nis an - ge - li - cus fit pa - nis ho - mi-num,
Au - thor of life di-vine, who hast a ta -ble spread,

Pa - nis an - ge- li-cus fit pa - nis ho-mi-num,
Au - thor of life di-vine, who hast a ta -ble spread,

* Alto part may be sung by a tenor or high baritone.

© Copyright 1994 by Kevin Mayhew Ltd.
It is illegal to photocopy music.

dat pa - nis coe - li - cus, fi - gu - ris ter - mi - num:
fur - nished with mys - tic wine and e - ver-last - ing bread:

dat pa - nis coe - li - cus, fi - gu - ris ter - mi - num:
fur - nished with mys - tic wine and e - ver-last - ing bread:

O res mi - ra - bi - lis, man - du - cat
our nee - dy souls sus-tain with fresh sup -

O res mi - ra - bi - lis, man - du - cat
our nee - dy souls sus-tain with fresh sup -

Do - mi - num, pau - per, pau - per, ser - vus et hu - mi-
plies of love, hear us, help us, till all thy life we

Do - mi - num, pau - per, pau - per et hu - mi-
plies of love, hear us, help us, till life we

pau - per, ser - vus et hu - mi -lis, pau - per,
help us, till all thy life we gain, hear and

pau - per, ser - vus et hu - mi -lis, pau -
hear us, till all thy life we gain, hear

pau - per, ser - vus, ser - vus et hu - mi - lis.
help us, till all, till all thy life we gain.

- per, ser - vus, ser - vus et hu - mi - lis.
us, till all, till all thy life we gain.

PANIS ANGELICUS (4-part)

Latin Text: Thomas Aquinas (1227-1274)
English Text: Charles Wesley (1707-1788) adapted by Neil Jenkins
Music: César Franck (1822-1890) arranged by Neil Jenkins

© Copyright 1994 by Kevin Mayhew Ltd.
It is illegal to photocopy music.

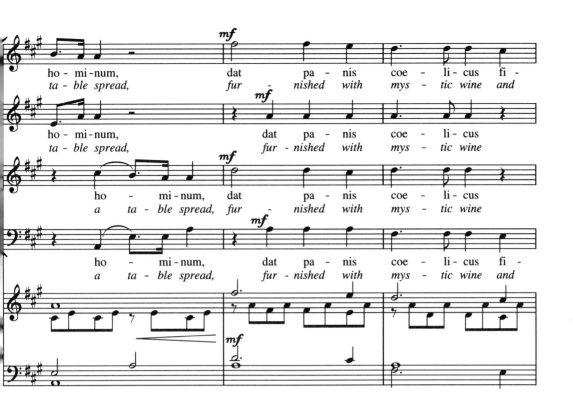

71

ra - bi -lis,   man - du - cat   Do - mi-num,
souls sus-tain   *with*   *fresh sup* - *plies of love.*

ra - bi -lis,   man - du - cat   Do - mi-num,
souls sus-tain   *with*   *fresh sup* - *plies of love.*

mi - ra - bi-lis,   man - du - cat   Do - mi-num,
souls   *sus-tain*   *with fresh*   *sup - plies of love.*

mi - ra - bi-lis,   man - du - cat   Do - mi-num,
souls   *sus-tain*   *with fresh*   *sup - plies of love.*

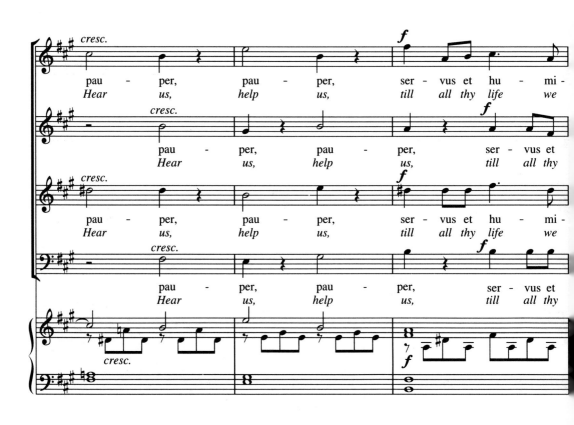

pau - per,   pau - per,   ser - vus et hu - mi -
Hear   *us,*   *help*   *us,*   *till all thy life*   *we*

pau - per,   pau - per,   ser - vus et
Hear   *us,*   *help*   *us,*   *till all thy*

pau - per,   pau - per,   ser - vus et hu - mi -
Hear   *us,*   *help*   *us,*   *till all thy life*   *we*

pau - per,   pau - per,   ser - vus et
Hear   *us,*   *help*   *us,*   *till all thy*

lis, pau - per, pau - per,
gain, hear us, help us,

hu - mi - lis, pau - per, pau -
life we gain, hear us, help

lis, pau - per, pau - per,
gain, hear us, help us,

hu - mi - lis, pau - per, pau -
life we gain, hear us, help

ser - vus et hu - mi - lis.
till all thy life we gain.

per, ser - vus et hu - mi - lis.
us, till all thy life we gain.

ser - vus et hu - mi - lis.
till all thy life we gain.

per, ser - vus et hu - mi - lis.
us, till all thy life we gain.

Man.

73

75

pau - per, ser - vus, ser-vus et hu - mi - lis.
help us, till all, till all thy life we gain.

pau - per, ser - vus, ser-vus et hu - mi - lis.
help us, till all, till all thy life we gain.

- per, ser - vus et hu - mi - lis.
us, help us, till life we gain.

- per, ser - vus et hu - mi - lis.
us, help us, till life we gain.

dim.

rall.

p

a tempo

Ped. ad lib.

morendo

Man.

TO THEE, O LORD, I YIELD MY SPIRIT

Text: J Schubring (from the oratorio *St Paul*)
Music: Felix Mendelssohn (1809-1847)

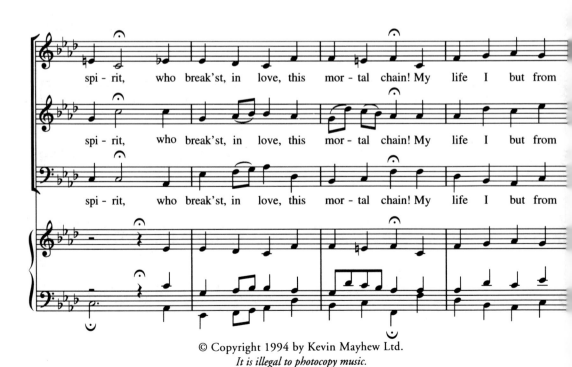

© Copyright 1994 by Kevin Mayhew Ltd.
It is illegal to photocopy music.

thee in - he - rit, and death be - comes my chief - est gain. In thee I

thee in - he - rit, and death be - comes my chief - est gain. In thee I

thee in - he - rit, and death be - comes my chief - est gain. In thee I

live, in thee I die. Con - tent, for thou art e - ver nigh.

live, in thee I die. Con - tent, for thou art e - ver nigh.

live, in thee I die. Con - tent, for thou art e - ver nigh.

I WILL LIFT UP MINE EYES

Text: Psalm 121

Music: Christopher Brown (*b.*1943)

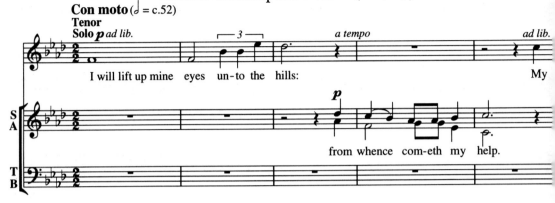

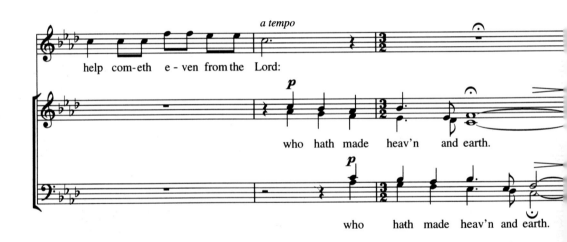

© Copyright 1994 by Kevin Mayhew Ltd.

It is illegal to photocopy music.

hold, he that keep-eth Is - ra- el:

Bass Solo *mf*

The

shall nei - ther slum-ber nor sleep.

shall nei - ther slum-ber nor sleep.

ad lib.   *a tempo*

Lord him-self is thy keep-er:

the Lord is thy de - fence up-on thy right hand.

Alto Solo *mf ad lib.*   *a tempo*

So that the sun shall not burn thee by day:

nei - ther the moon by night.

Faster *f*

The Lord shall pre - serve thee from all e - vil: yea, it is e - ven

THE BURIAL SERVICE

Text: from the *Book of Common Prayer*
Music: William Croft (1678-1727)

1. I am the resurrection and the life

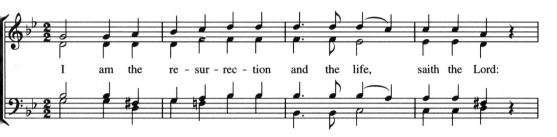

I am the re - sur - rec - tion and the life, saith the Lord:

he that be - liev - eth in me, though he were dead,

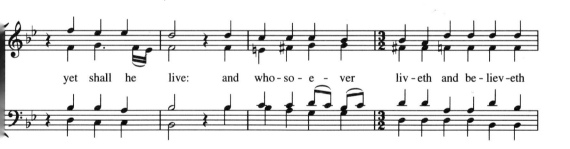

yet shall he live: and who - so - e - ver liv - eth and be - liev - eth

in me shall ne - ver die, shall ne - ver, shall ne - ver die.

© Copyright 1994 by Kevin Mayhew Ltd.
It is illegal to photocopy music.

2. I know that my Redeemer liveth

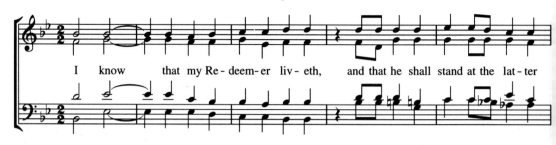

I know that my Re-deem-er liv-eth, and that he shall stand at the lat-ter

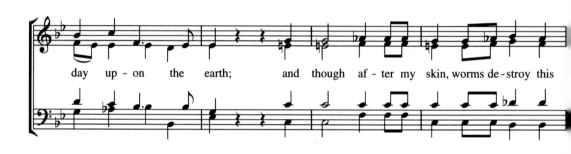

day up-on the earth; and though af-ter my skin, worms de-stroy this

bo-dy, yet in my flesh shall I see God, whom I shall see for my-

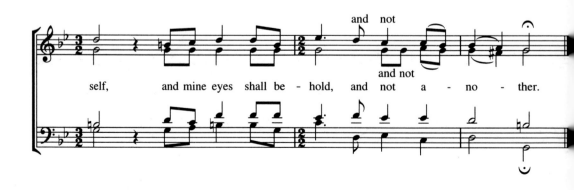

self, and mine eyes shall be-hold, and not a-no-ther.

and not

3. We brought nothing into this world

We brought no - thing in - to this world, and

it is cer - tain we can car - ry no - thing out. The Lord gave,

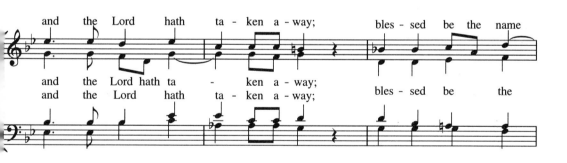

and the Lord hath ta - ken a - way; bles - sed be the name

and the Lord hath ta - ken a - way; bles - sed be the

and the Lord hath ta - ken a - way;

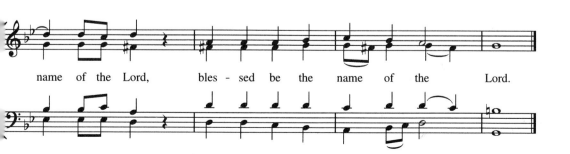

name of the Lord, bles - sed be the name of the Lord.

4. Man that is born of a woman

Man that is born of a wo - man hath but a short time to live, and is full of mi - se - ry, is full of mi - se - ry. He com - eth up and is cut down like a flow - er; he com - eth up, and is cut down like a flow - er; he flee - eth as it were a sha - dow, and ne - ver con - ti - nu - eth, ne - ver con - ti - nu - eth in one stay.

5. In the midst of life

In the midst of life we are in death: of whom may we seek for suc-cour, but of thee, of thee, O Lord, who for our sins art just-ly dis - pleas - ed? Yet, O Lord God most ho - ly, O

to the bit-ter, the bit - ter pains of e - ter - nal death.

not in - to the bit-ter pains of e - ter - nal death.

to the bit-ter, the bit-ter pains of e - ter - nal death.

to the bit-ter, the bit-ter pains of e - ter-nal death.

6. Thou knowest, Lord
Music: Henry Purcell (1659-1695)

Thou know-est, Lord, the se - crets of our hearts; shut not, shut not thy

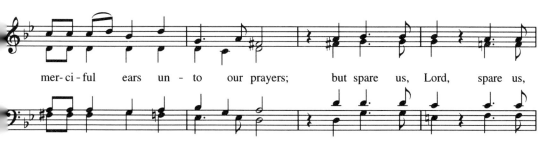

mer-ci-ful ears un - to our prayers; but spare us, Lord, spare us,

For an alternative setting of this text by Purcell, see page 192.

Lord most ho - ly, O God, O God most migh - ty, O ho - ly and most

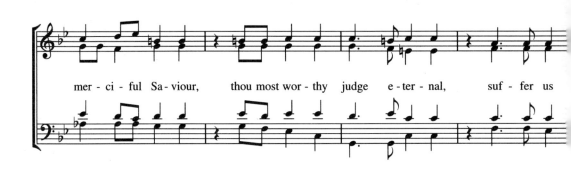

mer - ci - ful Sa - viour, thou most wor - thy judge e - ter - nal, suf - fer us

not, suf - fer us not, at our last hour for a - ny pains of death, for

for a - ny

(Organ)

for a - ny

a - ny pains of death, to fall, to fall from thee. A - men.

pains, for a - ny pains of death,

pains of death, to fall,

7. I heard a voice from heaven

I heard a voice from heav'n, from heav'n,

say - ing un - to me, write, from hence - forth bles - sed,

bles - sed are the dead which die in the Lord: ev'n

so saith the Spi - rit, for they rest from their la - bours.

so saith the Spi - rit, for they rest from their la - bours.

so saith the Spi - rit, for they rest from their la - bours.

so saith the Spi - rit, for they rest from their la - bours.

Ev'n so saith the Spi-rit, for they rest from their la - bours.

Ev'n so saith the Spi-rit, for they rest from their la-bours. A -

Ev'n so saith the Spi-rit, for they rest from their la - bours.

Ev'n so saith the Spi-rit, for they rest from their la -

LIFT THINE EYES

Text: Psalm 121: 1-3

Music: Felix Mendelssohn (1809-1847)

© Copyright 1994 by Kevin Mayhew Ltd.

It is illegal to photocopy music.

moved: thy keep-er will ne-ver slum - ber, ne-ver, will ne-ver slum - ber,

moved: thy keep-er will ne-ver slum - ber, ne-ver, will ne-ver

moved: thy keep-er will ne-ver slum - ber, ne-ver, will ne-ver

ne-ver slum - - ber. Lift thine eyes, O lift thine eyes

slum - - ber. Lift thine eyes, O lift thine eyes

slum - ber, will ne - ver slum - ber. Lift thine eyes, O lift thine eyes

to the moun - tains, whence com - eth, whence com - eth, whence com - eth

to the moun - tains, whence com - eth, whence com - eth, whence com - eth

to the moun - tains, whence com - eth, whence com - eth

help, whence com - eth, whence com - eth, whence com - eth help.

help, whence com - eth, whence com - eth, whence com - eth help.

help, whence com - eth, whence com - eth, whence com - eth help.

95

MORNING HAS BROKEN

Text: Eleanor Farjeon (1881-1965)
Music: Traditional Gaelic Melody arranged by Neil Jenkins

1. Morn-ing has bro-ken, like the first morn - ing; black-bird has spo - ken
2. Sweet the rain's new fall sun-lit from hea - ven, like the first dew - fall
3. Mine is the sun - light! Mine is the morn - ing born of the one light

like the first bird. Praise for the sing - ing! Praise for the morn - ing!
on the first grass. Praise for the sweet - ness of the wet gar - den,
E - den saw play! Praise with e - la - tion, praise ev -'ry morn - ing,

Praise for them, spring - ing fresh from the Word!
sprung in com - plete - ness where his feet pass.
God's re - cre - a - tion of the new day!

© Copyright David Higham Associates, from *The Children's Bells*,
published by Oxford University Press. Reproduced by permission.
It is illegal to photocopy music.

AND THEN SHALL COME
THE GLORIOUS MORN

Text: James Thomson (1700-1748) and
Gottfried van Swieten (1734-1803) adapted by Neil Jenkins
Music: Joseph Haydn (1732-1809)

© Copyright 1994 by Kevin Mayhew Ltd.

It is illegal to photocopy music.

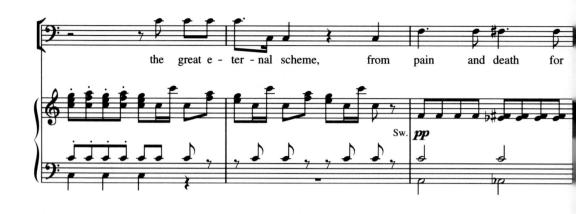

the great e - ter - nal scheme, from pain and death for

Tenor Solo

The

Bass Solo

e - ver free. The

heav'n - ly gates are lift - ed up, the ho - ly hill ap -

heav'n - ly gates are lift - ed up, the ho - ly hill ap -

pears,   there   on   the heav'n - ly   seat,   where

pears,   there   on   the heav'n - ly   seat,   where

peace   e - ter - nal dwells;   there on   the   heav'n-ly

peace   e - ter - nal dwells;   there on   the   heav'n-ly

seat,   where   peace   e - ter - - nal

seat,   where   peace   e - ter - - nal

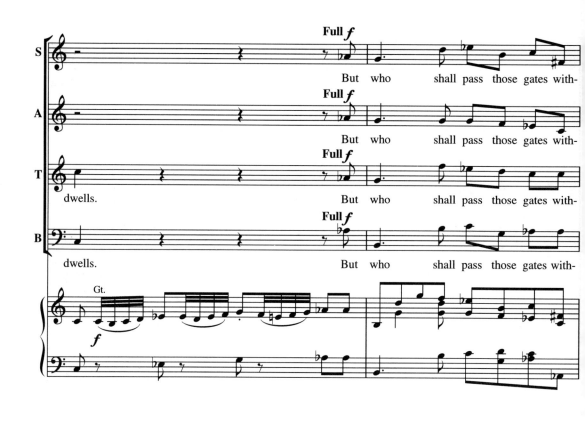

100

who dwell in that heav'n-ly place? The man whose heart was

who dwell in that heav'n-ly place?

who dwell in that heav'n-ly place? The man whose heart was

who dwell in that heav'n-ly place? The man whose heart was

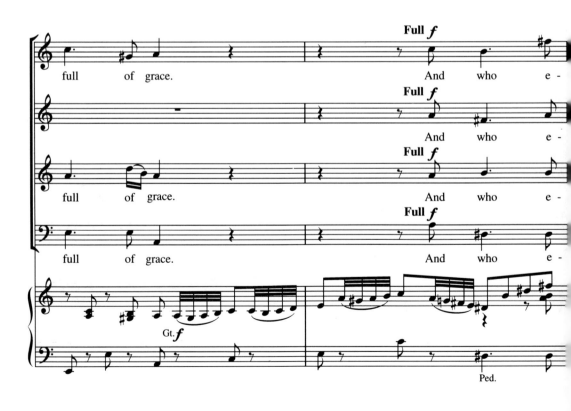

full of grace. And who e -

And who e -

full of grace. And who e -

full of grace. And who e -

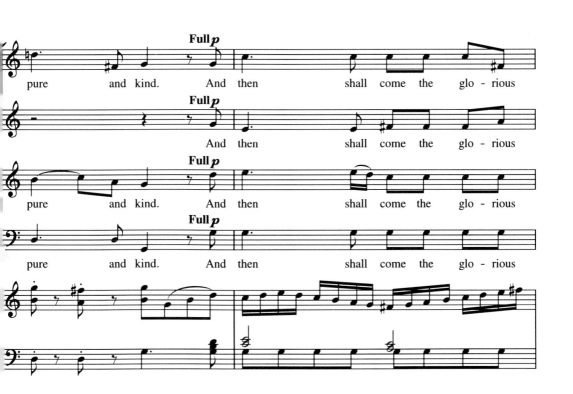

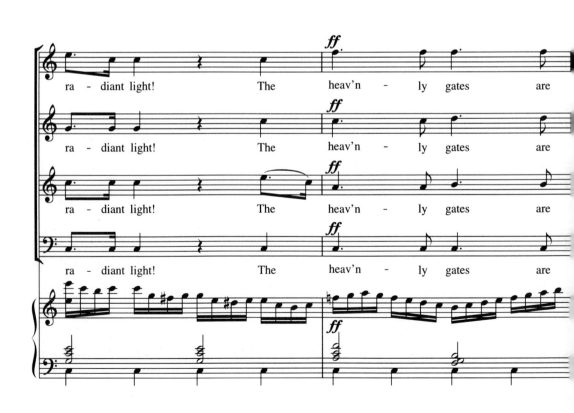

lift - ed up, the ho - ly hill ap -

lift - ed up, the ho - ly hill ap -

lift - ed up, the ho - ly hill ap -

lift - ed up, the ho - ly hill ap -

mf

pears. Now are they gone, and quick-ly past, the nights of doubt and

pears. Now are they gone, and quick-ly past, the nights of doubt and

pears. Now are they gone, and quick-ly past, the nights of doubt and

pears. Now are they gone, and quick-ly past, the nights of doubt and

Man.

Ped.

sor - row, the days of gloom and ter - ror. And one un - bound - ed

sor - row, the days of gloom and ter - ror. And one un - bound - ed

sor - row, the days of gloom and ter - ror. And one un - bound - ed

sor - row, the days of gloom and ter - ror. And one un - bound - ed

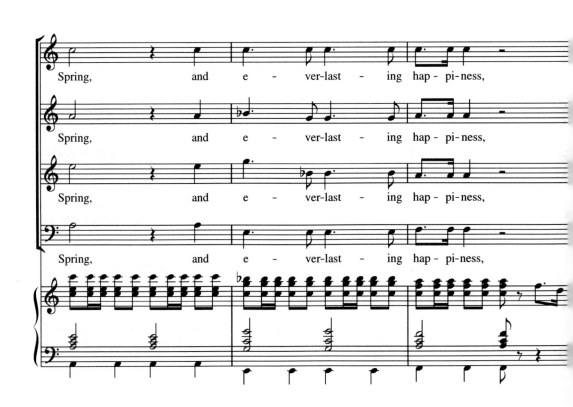

Spring, and e - ver-last - ing hap - pi - ness,

Spring, and e - ver-last - ing hap - pi - ness,

Spring, and e - ver-last - ing hap - pi - ness,

Spring, and e - ver-last - ing hap - pi - ness,

let us strug-gle,   let us bat-tle,   till we me - rit

let us strug-gle,   let us bat-tle,   till we me - rit

let us strug-gle,   let us bat-tle,   till we me - rit

let us strug-gle,   let us bat-tle,   till we me - rit

such   a prize.

such   a prize.

such   a prize.

such   a prize.

LEAD ME, LORD

Text: from Psalms 4, 5
Music: Samuel Sebastian Wesley (1810-1876)

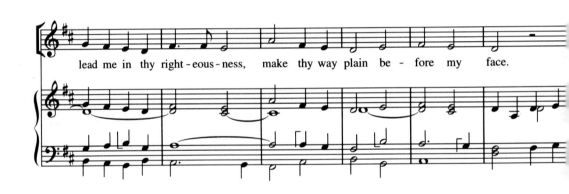

© Copyright 1994 by Kevin Mayhew Ltd.

It is illegal to photocopy music.

Soprano Solo

fore my face. For it is thou, Lord, thou, Lord, on - ly, that

Man.

mak - est me dwell in safe - ty. For it is thou, Lord,

Full *p*

p

Ped.

p

thou, Lord, on - ly, that mak - est me dwell in safe - ty.

rit.

p

rit.

p

O LOVELY PEACE

Text: Thomas Morell (1703-1784) adapted by Neil Jenkins
Music: George Frideric Handel (1685-1759)

O love - ly peace, with plen - ty crown'd,

O love - ly, love - ly peace, come spread thy bless- ings,

© Copyright 1994 by Kevin Mayhew Ltd.
It is illegal to photocopy music.

thy bless - ings all a - round;

mp

O love - ly peace, with plen - ty crown'd, O love - ly,

love - ly peace, come spread thy bless - ings, thy bless - ings

O love - ly, love - ly peace, O

all a - round; O, O love - ly,

love - ly peace, O love - ly, love - ly peace;

love - ly peace, O love - ly peace;

mf

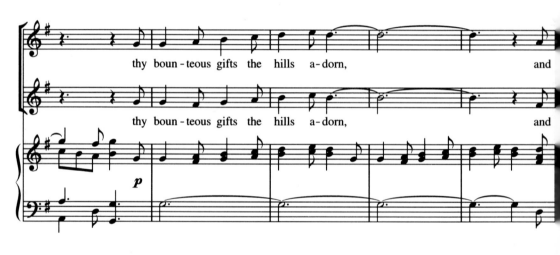

thy boun - teous gifts the hills a - dorn, and

thy boun - teous gifts the hills a - dorn, and

p

val - leys smile with wa - vy corn, thy

val - leys smile with wa - vy corn,

mf

p

wa - vy corn, with
with wa - vy corn, with wa - vy

wa - vy corn, with wa - vy corn;
corn, with wa - vy corn, with wa - vy
mf

thy boun - teous gifts the
corn; thy
p

hills a - dorn, the hills a - dorn, and

boun - teous gifts the hills a - dorn, the hills a - dorn, and

smile with wa - vy

smile with wa - vy

corn.

corn.

117

THE LORD'S PRAYER

Text: from the *Book of Common Prayer*
Music: Michael Head (1900-1976)

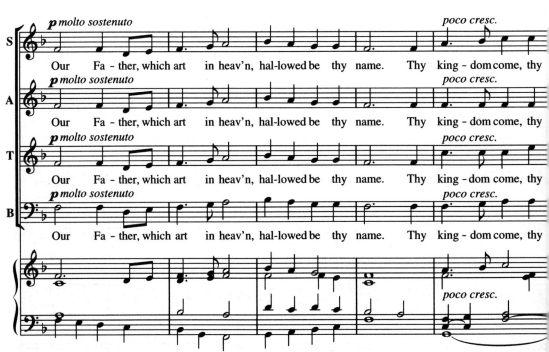

This piece may be sung as a solo or by unison
voices taking the Soprano line.

© Copyright 1956 by Boosey & Co Ltd. Reproduced by permission of
Boosey & Hawkes Music Publishers Ltd.
It is illegal to photocopy music.

119

us. Lead us not in-to temp-ta - tion; but de - li - ver us from

us. Lead us not in-to temp-ta - tion; but de - li - ver us from

us. Lead us not in-to temp-ta - tion; but de - li - ver us from

us. Lead us not in-to temp - ta - tion; but de -

Man.

Ped.

e - vil, de - li - ver us from e - vil. For thine is the

e - vil, de - li - ver us from e - vil. For thine is the

e - vil, de - li - ver us from e - vil. For thine is the

li - ver us from e - vil. For thine is the

king - dom, the power and the glo - ry, for e - ver and

king - dom, the power and the glo - ry, for e - ver and

king - dom, the power and the glo - ry, for e - ver and

king - dom, the power and the glo - ry, for e - ver and

e - ver. A - men, A - men.

e - ver. A - men, A - men.

e - ver. A - men, A - men.

e - ver. A - men.

AVE VERUM CORPUS

Text: 14th century
Music: Edward Elgar (1857-1934)

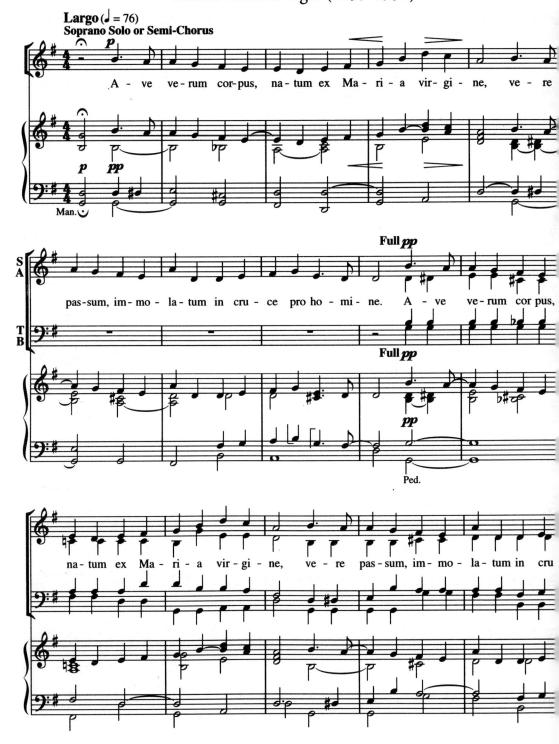

© Copyright 1994 by Kevin Mayhew Ltd.
It is illegal to photocopy music.

123

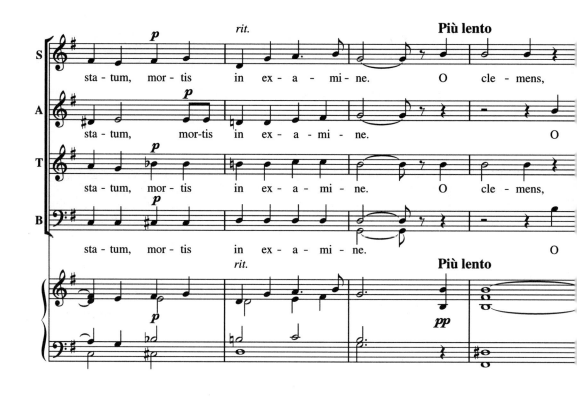

THE LORD IS MY SHEPHERD (SATB)

Text: Psalm 23
Music: Franz Schubert (1797-1828)
arranged by John Stainer (1840-1901)

© Copyright 1994 by Kevin Mayhew Ltd.
It is illegal to photocopy music.

shall not want, he is my

shall not want, he is my

shall not want, he is my

shall not want, he is my

shep - herd; I shall not, shall not want. He

shep - herd; I shall not, shall not want. He

shep - herd; I shall not, shall not want.

shep - herd; I shall not, shall not want.

lead - eth   me   be - side   still   wa - ters.

lead - eth   me   be - side   still   wa -   ters.

lead - eth   me   be - side   still   wa -   ters.

lead - eth   me   be - side   still   wa -   ters.

He   giv -   eth   peace   un - to   m

Ped.

128

soul: he lead - eth me in paths of

good - ness for his, for

his name's sake.

e - vil will I fear: for thou art still with

e - vil will I fear: for thou art still with

e - vil will I fear: for thou art still with

for thou art still with

Ped.

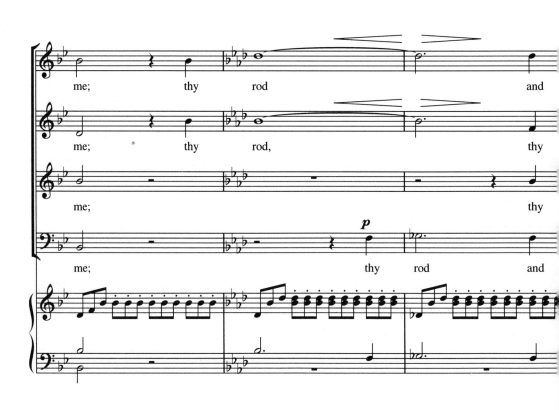

me; thy rod and

me; thy rod, thy

me; thy

me; thy rod and

staff,   thy rod   and staff they   com - fort, com - fort

rod   and staff, thy   rod   and staff they   com - fort, com - fort

staff,   thy   rod   and staff they   com - fort, com - fort

staff,   thy   rod   and staff they   com - fort, com - fort

me,   for thy   rod   and staff they com   -   fort

me,   for thy   rod   and staff they com   -   fort

me,   for thy   rod   and staff they com   -   fort

me,   for thy   rod   and staff they com   -   fort

o - ver. Yea, sure - ly peace and mer - cy all my life shall fol - low me: and I will

dwell   with God for e - ver, e   -   ver - more.   yea,

dwell   with God for e - ver, e   -   ver - more.   yea,

dwell   with God for e - ver, e   -   ver - more.   yea,

dwell   with God for e - ver, e   -   ver - more.   yea,

sure - ly peace and   mer - cy all   my   life   shall

sure - ly peace and   mer - cy all   my   life   shall

sure - ly peace and   mer -   - cy   shall

sure - ly peace and   mer - cy all   my   life   shall

e - - ver - more.

e - ver - more.

e - - ver - more.

e - - ver more.

ppp

THE LORD IS MY SHEPHERD (SA)

Text: Psalm 23

Music: Franz Schubert (1797-1828) arranged by Neil Jenkins

© Copyright 1994 by Kevin Mayhew Ltd.

It is illegal to photocopy music.

shep - herd; I shall not, shall not want. He

shep - herd; I shall not, shall not want. He

mak - eth me to rest in green pas - tures: he lead - eth me be -

mak - eth me to rest in green pas - tures: he lead - eth me be -

side still wa - ters, he mak - eth me to rest in green pas -tures, he

side still wa - ters, he mak - eth me to rest in green pas -tures, he

lead - eth me be - side still wa - ters.

lead - eth me be - side still wa - ters.

Man.

He giv - eth peace un - to my soul: he

He giv - eth peace un - to my soul: he

Ped.

lead - eth me in paths of good - ness for

lead - eth me in paths of good - ness for

143

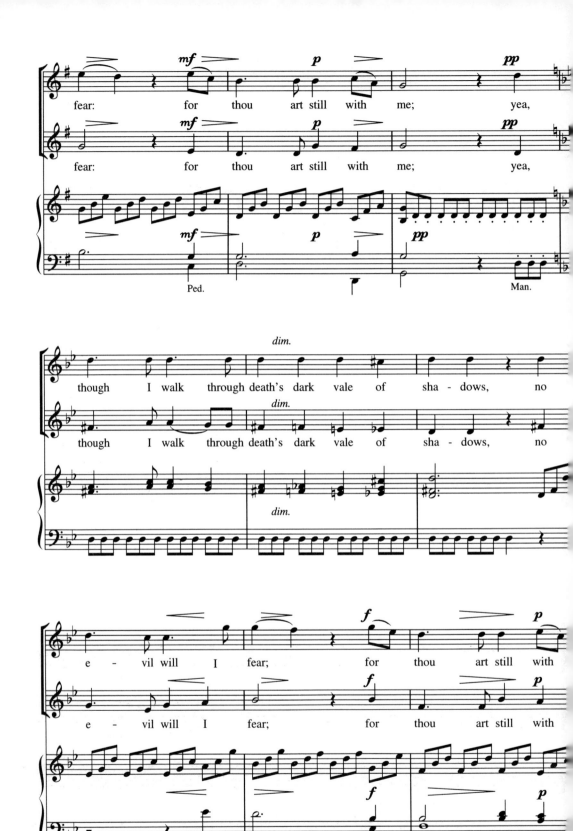

fear: for thou art still with me; yea,

though I walk through death's dark vale of sha - dows, no

e - vil will I fear; for thou art still with

me.

me.

Thou pre - par - est here a

Thou pre - par - est here a

ta - ble for me, in pre - sence of mine e - ne - mies: my

ta - ble for me, in pre - sence of mine e - ne - mies: my

head with oil thou a - noint - - est; my cup run-neth o - ver,

head with oil thou a - noint - est; my cup run-neth o - ver,

Man.

run - neth, run - neth o - ver. Yea, sure - ly peace and

run - neth, run - neth o - ver. Yea, sure - ly peace and

mer - cy all my life shall fol - low me:

mer - cy all my life shall fol - low me:

I will dwell with God for — e — ver,

I will dwell with God for e — ver,

e — — — ver — more.

e — — — ver — more.

Ped.

Man.

THE LORD IS MY SHEPHERD (SSAA)

Text: Psalm 23
Music: Franz Schubert (1797-1828)

© Copyright 1994 by Kevin Mayhew Ltd.
It is illegal to photocopy music.

shep - herd; I shall not, shall not want. He

shall not want.

shep - herd; I shall not, shall not want.

pp

mak - eth me to rest in green pas - tures: he lead - eth me be -

pp

He lead - eth me be -

he lead - eth me, he

side still wa - ters, he mak - eth me to rest in green pas -tures, he

side still wa - ters, he mak - eth me to rest in green pas -tures, he

Man.

151

leadeth me beside still waters.

leadeth me beside still waters.

He giveth peace unto my soul: he

He giveth peace unto my soul: he

leadeth me in paths of goodness for

leadeth me in paths of goodness for

me.

me.

p

Thou pre- par – est here a

p

Thou pre-

ta – ble for me, in pre - sence of mine e – ne - mies: my

par – est here a ta – ble for me: my

head with oil thou a - noint - est; my cup run-neth o - ver,

head with oil thou a - noint - est; my cup run-neth o - ver,

Man.

run - neth, run - neth o - ver. Yea, sure - ly peace and

run - neth, run - neth o - ver. Yea, sure - ly peace and

mer - cy all my life shall fol - low me:

mer - cy all my life shall fol - low me:

and I will dwell with God for e - ver, e - ver-

and I will dwell with God for e - ver, e - ver-

more, yea, sure - ly peace and mer - cy all my

mer - cy

more, yea, sure - ly peace and mer - cy all my

Man.

life shall fol - low me: and

life shall fol - low me: and

BLESSED ARE THE PURE IN HEART

Text: John Keble (1792-1866)
Music: Henry Walford Davies (1869-1941)

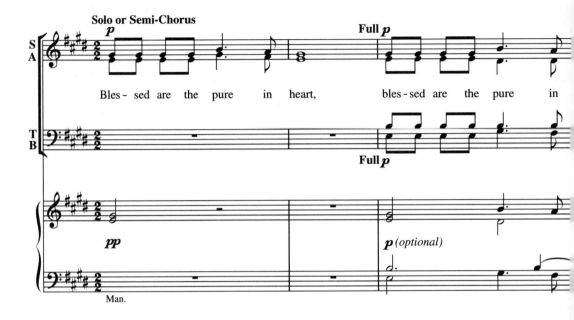

© Copyright 1994 by Kevin Mayhew Ltd.
It is illegal to photocopy music.

Lord is theirs, their soul is Christ's a - bode.

Still to the low - ly soul he doth him - self im - part, and

for his cra - dle and his throne choos - eth the pure in heart.

LET THEIR CELESTIAL
CONCERTS ALL UNITE

Text: John Milton (1608-1674)

Music: George Frideric Handel (1685-1759)

© Copyright 1994 by Kevin Mayhew Ltd.

It is illegal to photocopy music.

e - ver to sound his praise in end-less morn of

praise in end - less morn of

to sound his praise

light,

to sound his praise in end-less morn of

light,

let their ce-les-tial con-certs all u-nite, let their ce-les-tial con-certs

let their ce-les-tial con-certs all u-nite, let their ce-les-tial con-certs

light, let their ce-les-tial con-certs all u-nite, let their ce-les-tial con-certs

let their ce-les-tial con-certs all u-nite, let their ce-les-tial con-certs

Ped.

all u-nite, e-ver, e-ver, e-ver to sound his

all u-nite, e-ver, e-ver, e-ver to sound his

all u-nite, e-ver, e-ver, e-ver to sound his

all u-nite, to sound his praise

Man.

praise in end - less morn of light, to sound his praise,

praise in end - less morn of light, e - ver, e - ver,

praise in end - less morn of light, e - ver, e - ver,

in end - less morn of light, e - ver, e - ver,

to sound his praise in end-less morn, in

e - ver to sound, to sound his praise in end-less morn, in

e - ver to sound, to sound his praise in end-less morn of light, in

e - ver to sound, to sound his praise in end-less morn, in

165

let their ce - les - tial con-certs all u - nite,

let their ce - les - tial con-certs all u - nite,

e - ver to sound, to sound his praise in end - less morn

e - ver to sound, to sound his praise in end - less morn

e - ver to sound, to sound his praise in end - less morn

e - ver to sound his praise in end - less morn

Man.

Ped.

of light, in end - less morn of light,

of light, in end - less morn of light,

of light, in end - less morn of light,

of light, in end - less morn of light,

let their ce - les - tial con - certs all u - nite,

let their ce - les - tial con - certs all u - nite,

ff

e - ver to sound his praise in

e - ver, e - ver to sound his praise in

e - ver, e - ver to sound his praise in

e - ver, e - ver to sound his praise in

end - less morn of light.

end - less morn of light.

end - less morn of light.

end - less morn of light.

O WORSHIP THE KING

Text: Robert Grant (1779-1838)
Music: Wolfgang Amadeus Mozart (1756-1791)

O wor - ship the king, all glo - rious

* For SATB only version, cut to ⊕ on page 178.

© Copyright 1994 by Kevin Mayhew Ltd.
It is illegal to photocopy music.

bove,   O   grate – ful – ly   sing   of his   power   and his

love: our shield   and de – fend – er, the   an – cient of

days,   pa – vi – lioned in   splen – dour and   gird – ed   with

praise,   pa – vi – lioned in   splen – dour and   gird – ed   with

praise. Thy boun - ti - ful care

Man.

wha[t]

tongue can re - cite?

It breathes in the

air, and it shines in the light; it streams from the hills, it de -

Ped.

scends to the plain, and sweet - ly di - stils in the

dew and the rain, and sweet - ly di - stils in the

dew and the rain. Thy ran - somed cre - a - tion, though fee - ble their

lays, with true a-do - ra - tion shall sing to thy praise, shall sing to thy

for SA only version, cut to Coda

praise, shall sing to thy praise, shall sing to thy praise.

for SA only version, cut to Coda

praise. O wor - ship the king, all glo - rious a-

bove; O grate - ful - ly sing of his power and his

love: it streams from the hills, it de - scends to the plain, and

sweet - ly dis - tils in the dew and the rain, and

sweet - ly dis - tils in the dew and the rain. Thy

ran - somed cre - a - tion, though fee - ble their lays, with true a - do - ra - tion shall

179

sing to thy praise, shall sing to thy praise, shall sing to thy

praise, shall sing to thy praise.

Coda

Coda

THREE FUNERAL SENTENCES

Text: from the *Book of Common Prayer*

Music: Henry Purcell (1659-1695)

1. Man that is born of a woman

© Copyright 1994 by Kevin Mayhew Ltd.

It is illegal to photocopy music.

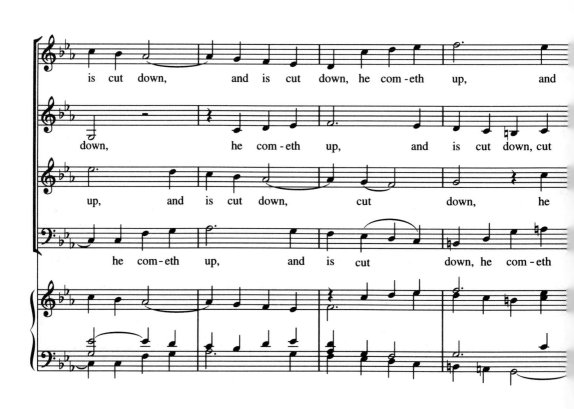

is cut down, and is cut down, like a flow'r; he

down, he com-eth up, and is cut down, like a flow'r; he

com-eth up, and is cut down, like a flow'r; he

up, and is cut down, and is cut down, like a flow'r; he

fleeth as it were a sha-dow, and ne'er con-ti-nu-eth,

fleeth as it were a sha-dow, and ne'er con-

fleeth as it were a sha-dow, and ne'er con-ti-nu-eth

fleeth as it were a sha-dow, and

Man.

183

185

ne'er con-ti-nu-eth, ne'er con-ti-nu-eth in one stay.

eth, ne'er con-ti-nu-eth in one stay, in one stay.

and ne'er con-ti-nu-eth in one stay.

ti-nu-eth, ne'er con-ti-nu-eth in one stay.

2. In the midst of life

In the midst of life we are in death;

In the midst of life

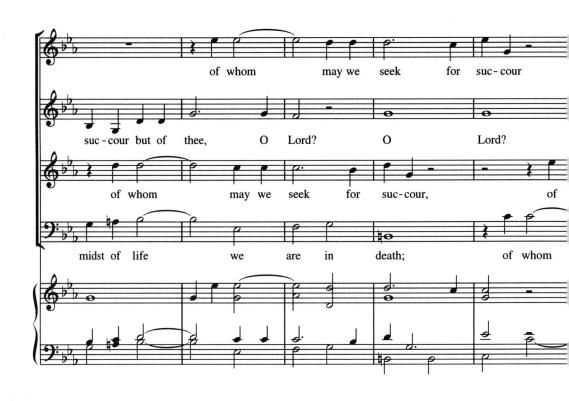

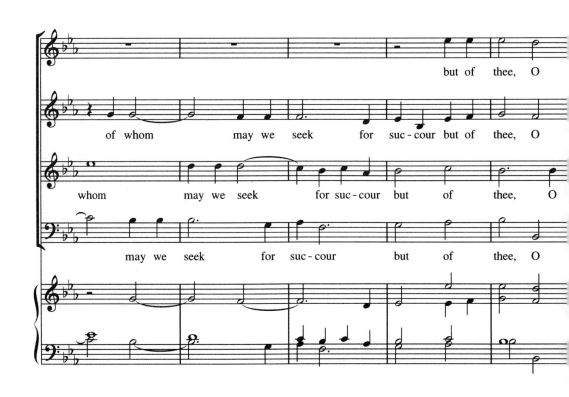

Lord? who for our sins art just - ly dis-

Lord? who for our sins art just - ly dis-

Lord? who for our sins, who for our sins art just - ly dis-

Lord? who for our sins, who for our sins art just - ly dis-

*(2nd time **Full**)*
pleas - ed. Yet, O Lord, O Lord most

*(2nd time **Full**)*
pleas - ed. Yet, O Lord, O Lord most

*(2nd time **Full**)*
pleas - ed. Yet, O Lord, O Lord most

*(2nd time **Full**)*
pleas - ed. Yet, O Lord, O Lord most

mighty, O ho - ly, O ho - ly and most mer - ci - ful Sa - vi -
mighty, O ho - ly, O ho - ly and most mer - ci - ful Sa - vi -
mighty, O ho - ly, O ho - ly and most mer - ci - ful Sa - vi -
mighty, O ho - ly, O ho - ly and most mer - ci - ful Sa - vi -

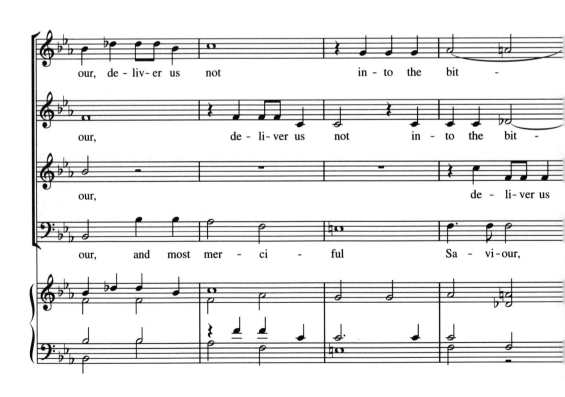

our, de - liv - er us not into the bit -
our, de - li - ver us not in - to the bit -
our, de - li - ver us
our, and most mer - ci - ful Sa - vi - our,

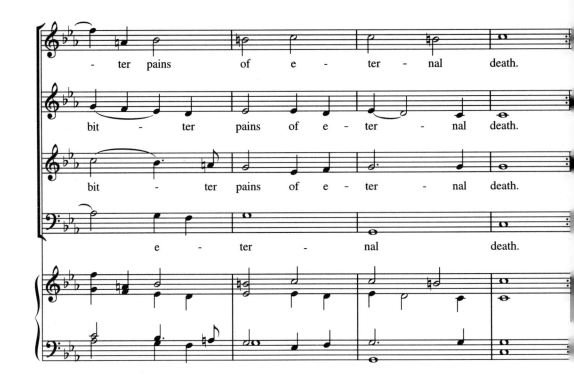

3. Thou know'st Lord

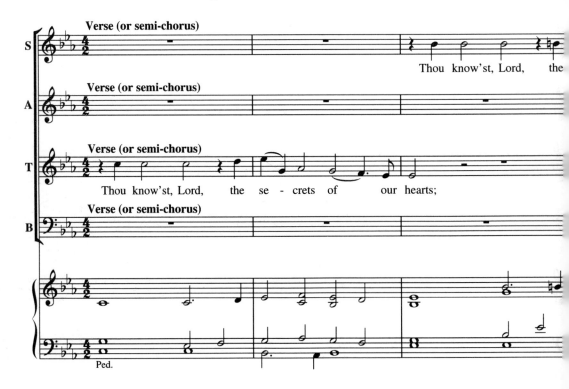

se - crets of our hearts;

Thou know'st, Lord, the se - crets of our

Thou know'st, Lord, the se - crets of our

shut not, shut not thy mer - ci - ful ears, thy mer - ci - ful ears, thy

hearts;

shut not thy mer - ci - ful ears,

hearts; shut not, shut not, shut not thy

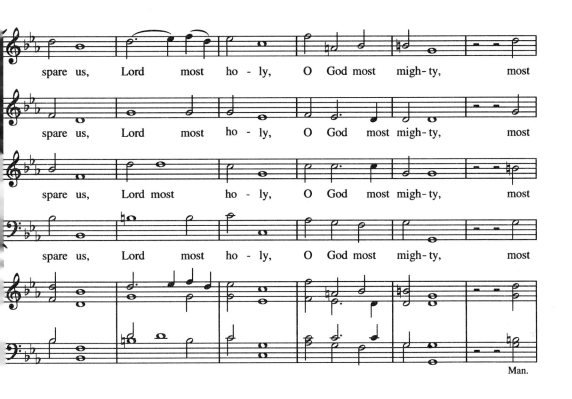

spare us, Lord most ho - ly, O God most migh-ty, most

spare us, Lord most ho - ly, O God most migh-ty, most

spare us, Lord most ho - ly, O God most migh-ty, most

spare us, Lord most ho - ly, O God most migh-ty, most

Man.

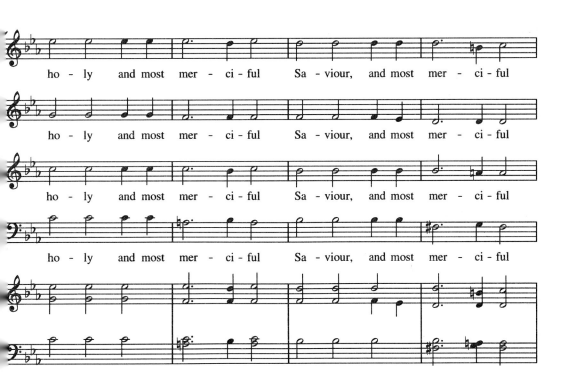

ho - ly and most mer - ci - ful Sa - viour, and most mer - ci - ful

ho - ly and most mer - ci - ful Sa - viour, and most mer - ci - ful

ho - ly and most mer - ci - ful Sa - viour, and most mer - ci - ful

ho - ly and most mer - ci - ful Sa - viour, and most mer - ci - ful

Sa - viour, thou most wor - thy judge, thou most wor - thy judge e -

Sa - viour, thou most wor - thy judge, thou most wor - thy judge e -

Sa - viour, thou most wor- thy judge, thou most wor - thy judge e -

Sa - viour, thou most wor - thy judge, thou most wor - thy judge e -

Ped.

(2nd time **Full***)*

ter - nal, suf - fer us not at our last hour, at our last hour, our

(2nd time **Full***)*

ter - nal, suf - fer us not at our last hour, at our last hour, our

(2nd time **Full***)*

ter - nal, suf - fer us not at our last hour, at our last hour, our

(2nd time **Full***)*

ter - nal, suf - fer us not at our last hour, at our last hour, our

last hour, for a - ny pains of death, to fall, to

last hour, for a - ny pains of death, to fall,

last hour, for a - ny pains of death, to fall,

last hour, for a - ny pains of death, to fall,

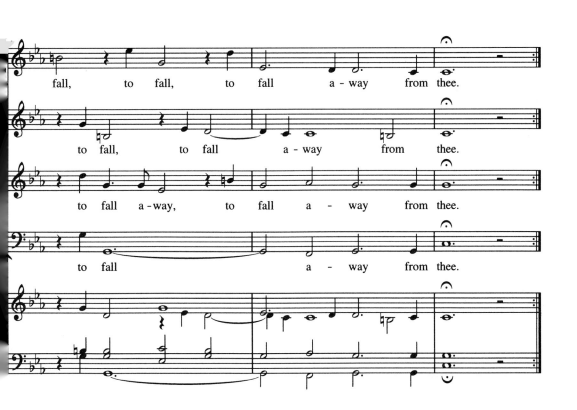

fall, to fall, to fall a - way from thee.

to fall, to fall a - way from thee.

to fall a - way, to fall a - way from thee.

to fall a - way from thee.

AVE MARIA

Latin Text: from Luke 1
English Text: Neil Jenkins
Music: Charles Gounod (1818-1893) arranged by Colin Mawby (*b.*1936)

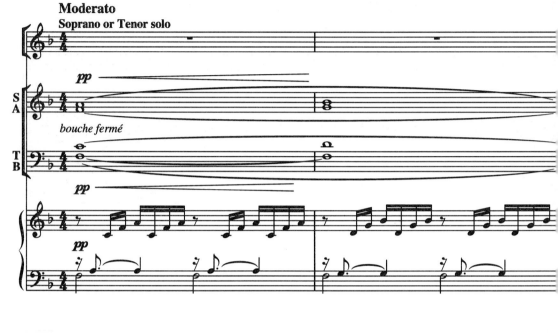

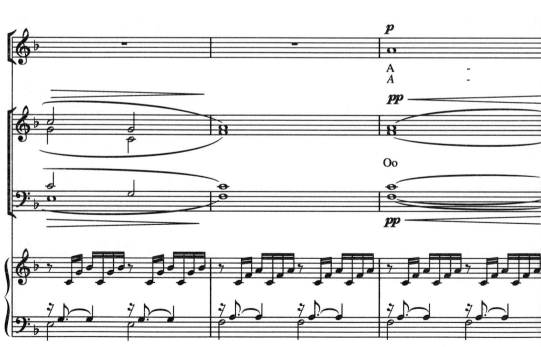

© Copyright 1994 by Kevin Mayhew Ltd.
It is illegal to photocopy music.

ve Ma - ri a,
ve *Ma - ri* *a,*

gra - ti - a ple - na, Do - mi -nus
mai - *den* *pure* *and mild,* *mo* - *ther of the*

Oo   Oo

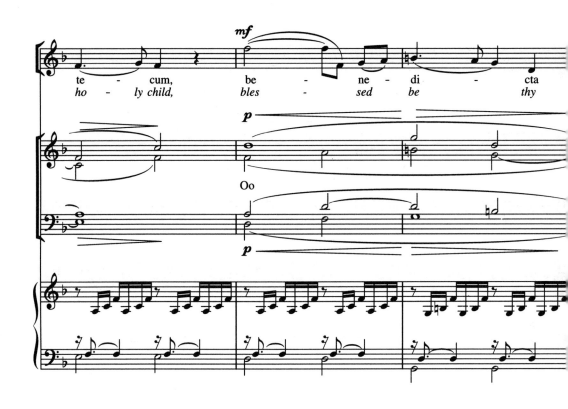

te - cum, be - ne - di - cta
ho - ly child, bles - sed be thy

Oo

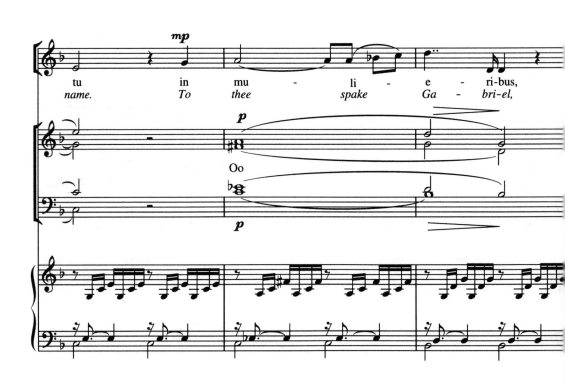

tu in mu - li - e - ri-bus,
name. To thee spake Ga - bri-el,

Oo

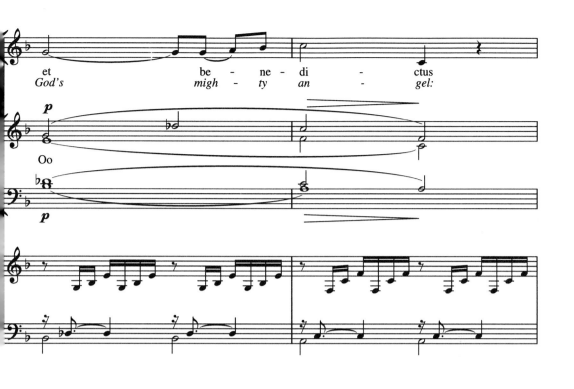

et ____ be – ne – di ____ ctus
God's ____ migh – ty an ____ gel:

Oo

cresc.

fru – ctus ven – tris tu – i, Je –
'Hail, high – ly fa – voured, full of grace art

Oo

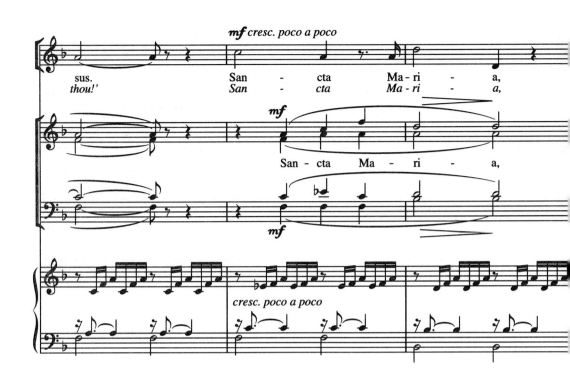

ho - ra mor - tis no - strae. A -
e - ver, world with - out end. A -

men. A - men.
men. A - men.
A - - men.

A SHORT REQUIEM

Text: from various sources
Music: Henry Walford Davies (1869-1941)

1. O Saviour of the World

O sa - viour, sa - viour of the world, O sa - viour, sa - viour of the world, who by thy cross, by thy cross and pre - cious blood hast re - deem- ed us, who by thy cross and pre - cious blood hast re - deem- ed us: save us, save us and help us, save us and help us, save and help us, we hum - bly be-seech thee, O Lord, we hum - bly be-seech thee, O Lord.

from *The Book of Common Prayer*

© Copyright 1994 by Kevin Mayhew Ltd.
It is illegal to photocopy music.

2. Out of the deep (Psalm 130)

1. Out of the deep have I called unto | thee, O | Lord:
   Lord, | hear | my | voice.

2. O let thine ears con-| sider | well:
   The | voice of | my com-| plaint.

3. If thou Lord wilt be extreme to mark what is | done a-| miss:
   O | Lord, who | may a-| bide it?

4. For there is | mercy · with | thee:
   There-| fore shalt | thou be | feared.

5. I look for the Lord, my | soul doth | wait for him:
   In | his word | is my | trust.

6. My soul fleeth | unto · the | Lord:
   Before the morning watch I say, be-| fore the | morning | watch.

7. O Israel trust in the Lord, for with the Lord | there is | mercy:
   And with him is | plen-| teous re-| demption:

8. And he shall re-| deem | Israel:
   From | all | his | sins.

At a funeral, instead of the Gloria, sing the following Requiem Aeternam.

3. Requiem Aeternam (I)

Re - qui - em æ - ter - nam do - na
e - is, do - na e - is Do - mi - ne,
et lux per - pe - tu - a lu - ce - at e - is.
Re - qui-em æ - ter - nam do - na e - is Do - mi-ne.

From the *Requiem Mass*

If being used at a service other than a funeral, the normal Gloria should be sung.

4. I will lift up mine eyes (Psalm 121)

1. I will lift up mine eyes | unto the | hills:
   From | whence | cometh · my | help.

2. My help cometh even | from the | Lord:
   Who | hath made | heaven and | earth.

3. He will not suffer thy | foot to · be | moved:
   And he that | keepeth · thee | will not | sleep.

4. Behold, he that | keepeth | Israel:
   Shall | neither | slumber · nor | sleep.

5. The Lord himself | is thy | keeper:
   The Lord is thy de-| fence up · on | thy right | hand;

6. So that the sun shall not | burn thee · by | day:
   Nei-| ther the | moon by | night.

7. The Lord shall preserve thee | from all | evil:
   Yea, it is even | he · that shall | keep thy | soul.

8. The Lord shall preserve thy going out, and thy | coming | in:
   From this time | forth for | ever-| more.

At a funeral, instead of the Gloria, sing the following Requiem Aeternam.

5. Requiem Aeternam (II)

If being used at a service other than a funeral, the normal Gloria should be sung.

6. I heard a voice from heaven

Revelation 14:13

210

7. No more to sigh

1. No more to sigh, no more to weep, the faith - ful dead in
2. Though in the grave their clay is cold, they have not left the
3. An an - gel sings that they are blest; yea, saith the Spi - rit,

Je - sus sleep: un - fad - ing let their mem - 'ry bloom, while
Chris - tian fold; still we are shar - ers of their joy, com -
sweet their rest; in bow'rs of par - a - dise they meet, se -

rest their bo - dies in the tomb; nor will the Lord their
pan - ions of their blest em - ploy; and thee in them, O
cure be - neath their Sa - viour's feet, nor fear the trump that

love dis - trust that strews its gar - lands o'er their dust.
Lord most high, and them in thee we mag - ni - fy.
soon shall all be - fore the throne of judge - ment call.

8. Glory be to the Father

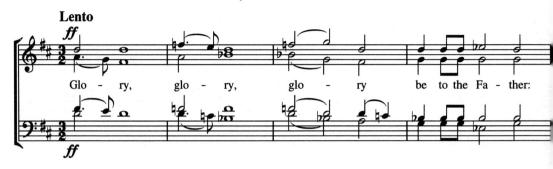

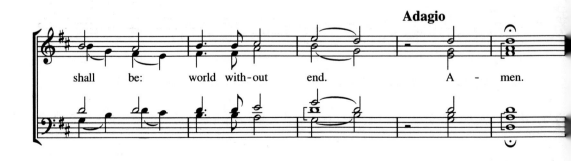

9. Tarry no longer

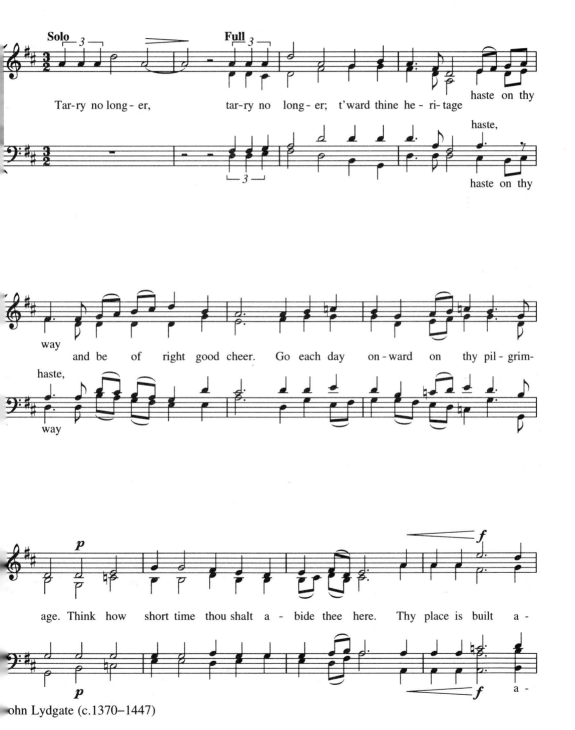

Tar-ry no long-er, tar-ry no long-er; t'ward thine he-ri-tage haste on thy way and be of right good cheer. Go each day on-ward on thy pil-grim-age. Think how short time thou shalt a - bide thee here. Thy place is built a -

haste, haste on thy way

haste, way

a -

John Lydgate (c.1370–1447)

213

bove the star - re's clear; none earth - ly pa - lace wrought in so state - ly

bove the stars

wise. Come on my friend, my bro - ther most dear! Come on, my

friend, my bro - ther most dear! For thee I

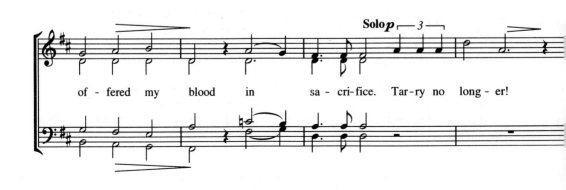

of - fered my blood in sa - cri - fice. Tar - ry no long - er!

THE LORD'S MY SHEPHERD (Crimond)

Text: Psalm 23

Music: Jessie Irvine (1836-1887) harmonized by Neil Jenkins
with descant by W Baird Ross

The Lord's my shep - herd, I'll not want. He
makes me down to lie in pas - tures green. He
lead - eth me the qui - et wa - ters by.

2. My soul he doth restore again,
and me to walk doth make
within the paths of righteousness,
e'en for his own name's sake.

3. Yea, though I walk in death's dark vale,
yet will I fear none ill.
For thou art with me, and thy rod
and staff me comfort still.

4. My table thou hast furnishèd
in presence of my foes;
my head thou dost with oil anoint,
and my cup overflows.

5. Goodness and mercy all my life
shall surely follow me.
And in God's house for evermore
my dwelling-place shall be.

Descant © Copyright Novello & Co. Reproduced by permission.
It is illegal to photocopy music.

AVE VERUM CORPUS

Latin Text: 14th century
English Text: H N Oxenham (1829-1888)
Music: Wolfgang Amadeus Mozart (1756-1791)

© Copyright 1994 by Kevin Mayhew Ltd.

It is illegal to photocopy music.

cru – ce pro ho – mi – ne.
deem-er of the sons of earth.

Cu – jus la – tus per – fo – ra – tum
Thou whose side be – came a foun – tain

un – da flux – it et san – gui – ne.
pour – ing forth thy pre – cious blood.

mor - - - - tis ex -
Je - - - - *su,* *bles - sed*

in mor - - - tis ex -
O *Je* - - - *su,* *bles - sed*

in mor - - - tis ex -
O *Je* - - - *su,* *bles - sed*

in mor - - - tis ex -
O *Je* - - - *su,* *bles - sed*

Ped.

a - mi - ne.
Ma - *ry's* *son.*

a - mi - ne.
Ma - *ry's* *son.*

a - mi - ne.
Ma - *ry's* *son.*

a - mi - ne.
Ma - *ry's* *son.*

O PRAISE GOD IN HIS HOLINESS

Text: Psalm 150
Music: Charles Stanford (1852-1924)

© Copyright 1994 by Kevin Mayhew Ltd.

It is illegal to photocopy music.

6. Let everything that hath breath: praise the Lord.

Glory be to the Father and to the Son: and to the Ho - ly Ghost;

As it was in the beginning,
is now and e - ver shall be: world without end. A - - - men.

MY FRIEND IS MINE

Text: Philipp Nicolai translated by Georgina Troutbeck
Music: Johann Sebastian Bach (1685-1750)

Text: © Copyright Control
Music: © Copyright 1994 by Kevin Mayhew Ltd.
It is illegal to photocopy music.

love   no   pow'r   shall   sun -   der.

love   no   pow'r   shall   sun - der, shall sun - der.

My friend is mine!

and

223

friend is mine, our love no pow'r

thine, and I am thine, our love no

shall sun - der, my friend is

pow'r shall sun - der, and

mine, our love no pow'r shall sun - der, my friend is

I am thine, and I am thine, and

mine,   our love

and I am   thine,   our love   no

no pow'r shall sun - der.

pow'r shall sun -   der.

CONTAKION OF THE FAITHFUL DEPARTED

Text: translated from the Russian by W J Birkbeck (1869-1916)
Music: Traditional Kiev

Give rest, O Christ, to thy ser-vant with thy saints; where sor-row and pain are no more; nei-ther sigh-ing, but life e-ver-last-ing.

Thou on-ly art im-mor-tal, the cre-a-tor and ma-ker of man: and we are mor-tal, form-ed of the earth,

© Copyright 1994 by Kevin Mayhew Ltd.
It is illegal to photocopy music.

and un - to earth shall we re - turn: for so thou didst or - dain, when thou cre - a - tedst me, say - ing: dust thou art, and un - to dust shalt thou re - turn. All we go down to the dust; and, weep - ing o'er the grave, we make our song, Al - le - lu - ia! Al - le - lu - ia! Al - le - lu - ia!

D.C. al Fine

O FOR THE WINGS OF A DOVE

Text: Psalm 55: 6, 7
Music: Felix Mendelssohn (1809-1847)

© Copyright 1994 by Kevin Mayhew Ltd.
It is illegal to photocopy music.

nest, and re-main there for e - ver at rest, in the wil-der-ness build me,

build me a nest, and re - main there for e - ver at rest, in the wil-der-ness

build me a nest, and re - main there for e - ver at rest, and re-main there for

e - ver at rest, and re-main there for e - ver at

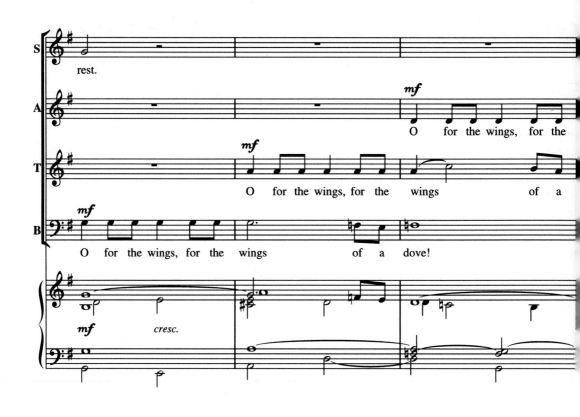

build me a nest, and re-main there for e-ver at rest,

nest, and re-main there for e-ver at rest, re-

wil-der-ness build me a nest, and re-main there for e-ver at

way! In the

and re-main there for e-ver at rest, re-main

main there for e-ver, for e-ver at rest, re-main

rest, and re-main there for e-ver, for e-ver at rest, re-main

wil-der-ness build me a nest, and re-main there at rest, re-main

there for e - ver at rest, re - main there for e - ver at rest, for e - ver at

there for e - ver at rest, re - main there for e - ver at rest, for e - ver at

there for e - ver at rest, re - main there for e - ver at rest, for e - ver at

there for e - ver at rest, re - main there for e - ver at rest, for e - ver at

O for the wings, for the wings of a dove! Far a - way, far a -

rest,

rest,

rest,

rest,

LAUDATE DOMINUM

Text: Psalm 117

Music: Wolfgang Amadeus Mozart (1756-1791)

© Copyright 1994 by Kevin Mayhew Ltd.

It is illegal to photocopy music.

Quo - ni-am con - fir - ma - ta est su - per
For he has shown to - ward us e - ver-

nos mi - se - ri - cor - di - a
more and more his mer - ci-ful

e - jus,
kind - ness.

et
O

Solo

Sw.

ve - ri - tas, ve - ri-tas Do - mi - ni
praise the Lord, all ye peo - ple.

ma - net, ma - net
His truth shall en -

in ae - ter -
dure for e -

num. Glo - ri - a pa - tri et
ver. Glo - ry be to the Fa - ther and

Glo - ri - a pa - tri et
Glo - ry be to the Fa - ther and

Glo - ri - a pa - tri et
Glo - ry be to the Fa - ther and

Glo - ri - a pa - tri et
Glo - ry be to the Fa - ther and

Glo - ri - a pa - tri et
Glo - ry be to the Fa - ther and

Gt.

Soloist may remain tacet until 'Amen' if desired.
When sung as a solo, the soloist should continue singing the soprano part as printed.

JESU, JOY OF MAN'S DESIRING

Text: Robert Bridges (1844-1930)
Music: Johann Sebastian Bach (1685-1750)
arranged by Malcolm Archer (*b.*1952)

1. Je - su, joy of man's de - sir - ing,
2. Through the way, where hope is guid - ing,

© Copyright 1994 by Kevin Mayhew Ltd.
It is illegal to photocopy music.

ho - ly wis - dom, love most
hark, what peace - ful music

bright,
rings,

drawn by thee, our souls as - pir - ing,
where the flock, in thee con - fid - ing,

soar to un - cre - a - ted light.
drink of joy from death - less springs.

round   thy   throne.
joys   un -   known.

THE SOULS OF THE RIGHTEOUS

Text: Book of Wisdom
Music: Henry Walford Davies (1869-1941)

© Copyright 1994 by Kevin Mayhew Ltd.
It is illegal to photocopy music.

255

touch them. They are in peace,
touch them. They are in peace,
touch them. They are in peace,
touch them. They are in peace, they
touch them. They are in peace,

they are in peace.
they are in peace.
they are in peace.
they are in peace.
they are in peace.

THEY SHALL BE AS HAPPY (4-part)

Text: Elkanah Settle (1648-1724)
Music: Henry Purcell (1659-1695)

Allegro moderato

© Copyright 1994 by Kevin Mayhew Ltd.
It is illegal to photocopy music.

love shall fill all, all, all the pla - ces of care; care;

love shall fill all, all, all the pla - ces of care; care;

love shall fill all, all, all the pla - ces of care; care;

love shall fill all, all, all the pla - ces of care; care;

Ped.

and ev - 'ry time the sun shall dis - play his ris -

and ev - 'ry time the sun shall dis - play his ris -

and ev - 'ry time the sun shall dis - play his ris -

and ev - 'ry time the sun shall dis - play his ris -

Man.

- ing light, it shall be to them a new wed-ding day; and

- ing, ris - ing light, it shall be to them a new wed - ding day; and

- ing, ris - ing light, it shall be to them a new wed-ding day; and

- ing, ris - ing light, it shall be to them a new wed-ding day; and

Ped.

when he sets, and when he sets, a new, a new nup - tial night.

when he sets, and when he sets, a new, a new nup - tial night.

when he sets, and when he sets, a new, a new nup - tial night.

when he sets, and when he sets, a new, a new nup - tial night.

THEY SHALL BE AS HAPPY (3-part)

Text: Elkanah Settle (1648-1724)
Music: Henry Purcell (1659-1695)

Allegro moderato

They shall be as hap-py, hap-py as they're fair; love, love shall fill all, all,

They shall be as hap-py, hap-py as they're fair; love, love shall fill all, all,

They shall be as hap-py, hap-py as they're fair; love, love shall fill all, all,

© Copyright 1994 by Kevin Mayhew Ltd.
It is illegal to photocopy music.

Index of Uses

Page

UNISON VOICES

Jerusalem	Hubert Parry	23
The Lord's Prayer	Michael Head	118

SOLO(S) WITH CHORUS

Agnus Dei	Wolfgang Amadeus Mozart	36
And then shall come the glorious morn	Joseph Haydn	97
Ave Maria	Charles Gounod	198
Come, Holy Ghost	Thomas Attwood	60
Laudate Dominum	Wolfgang Amadeus Mozart	240
Lead me, Lord	Samuel Sebastian Wesley	110
O for the wings of a dove	Felix Mendelssohn	230
The Lost Chord	Arthur Sullivan	26

TWO-PART

Brother James's Air (SS or SA)	Gordon Jacob	12
Love one another (SS or SA)	Samuel Sebastian Wesley	7
My friend is mine (SB)	Johann Sebastian Bach	222
O lovely peace (SS, SA or ST)	George Frideric Handel	112
O worship the King (SS or SA)	Wolfgang Amadeus Mozart	174
Panis Angelicus (SS, SA, ST or SB)	César Franck	65
The Lord is my shepherd (SA)	Franz Schubert	140

THREE-PART

Lift thine eyes (SSA)	Felix Mendelssohn	94
Nunc Dimittis (SAT)	Christopher Brown	47
They shall be as happy (SAB)	Henry Purcell	260
To thee, O Lord, I yield my spirit (STB or ATB)	Felix Mendelssohn	78

FOUR-PART (SATB)

Ave verum corpus	Edward Elgar	122
Ave verum corpus	Wolfgang Amadeus Mozart	216
Blessed are the pure in heart	Henry Walford Davies	160
Bridegroom and Bride	Arthur Sullivan	54
Cast thy burden upon the Lord	Felix Mendelssohn	52
Contakion of the Faithful Departed	Traditional Kiev	228
God be in my head	Henry Walford Davies	58
I will lift up mine eyes	Christopher Brown	80

		Page
Jesu, joy of man's desiring	Johann Sebastian Bach	248
Let their celestial concerts all unite	George Frideric Handel	162
Lo, thus shall the man be blessed	George Frideric Handel	16
Morning has broken	Traditional Gaelic	96
Nunc Dimittis	Christopher Brown	47
O praise God in his holiness	Charles Stanford	220
O worship the King	Wolfgang Amadeus Mozart	174
Panis Angelicus	César Franck	70
Since by man came death	George Frideric Handel	33
The Burial Service	William Croft	83
The Lord is my shepherd	Franz Schubert	125
The Lord is my shepherd (SSAA)	Franz Schubert	150
The Lord's my shepherd (Crimond)	Jessie Irvine	215
The Lord's Prayer	Michael Head	118
They shall be as happy	Henry Purcell	257
Three Funeral Sentences	Henry Purcell	181
To thee, O Lord, I yield my spirit	Felix Mendelssohn	78

OTHER COMBINATIONS

God be in my head (SSATBB)	Henry Walford Davies	59
The souls of the righteous (SSATBB)	Henry Walford Davies	254

ITEMS SUITABLE FOR WEDDINGS

Agnus Dei	Wolfgang Amadeus Mozart	36
Bridegroom and Bride	Arthur Sullivan	54
Lo, thus shall the man be blessed	George Frideric Handel	16
Love one another	Samuel Sebastian Wesley	7
My friend is mine	Johann Sebastian Bach	222
They shall be as happy (3-part)	Henry Purcell	260
They shall be as happy (4-part)	Henry Purcell	257

ITEMS SUITABLE FOR FUNERALS AND MEMORIAL SERVICES

A Short Requiem	Henry Walford Davies	205
And then shall come the glorious morn	Joseph Haydn	97
Cast thy burden upon the Lord	Felix Mendelssohn	52
Contakion of the Faithful Departed	Traditional Kiev	228
Nunc Dimittis	Christopher Brown	47
Since by man came death	George Frideric Handel	33

		Page
The Burial Service	William Croft	83
The Lost Chord	Arthur Sullivan	26
The souls of the righteous	Henry Walford Davies	254
Three Funeral Sentences	Henry Purcell	181
To thee, O Lord, I yield my spirit	Felix Mendelssohn	78

ITEMS SUITABLE FOR ANY CHURCH CELEBRATION

Agnus Dei	Wolfgang Amadeus Mozart	36
Ave Maria	Charles Gounod	198
Ave verum corpus	Edward Elgar	122
Ave verum corpus	Wolfgang Amadeus Mozart	216
Blessed are the pure in heart	Henry Walford Davies	160
Brother James's Air	Gordon Jacob	12
Come, Holy Ghost	Thomas Attwood	60
God be in my head (4-part)	Henry Walford Davies	58
God be in my head (6-part)	Henry Walford Davies	59
I will lift up mine eyes	Christopher Brown	80
I will lift up mine eyes	Henry Walford Davies	208
Jerusalem	Hubert Parry	23
Jesu, joy of man's desiring	Johann Sebastian Bach	248
Laudate Dominum	Wolfgang Amadeus Mozart	240
Lead me, Lord	Samuel Sebastian Wesley	110
Let their celestial concerts all unite	George Frideric Handel	162
Lift thine eyes	Felix Mendelssohn	94
Morning has broken	Traditional Gaelic	96
O for the wings of a dove	Felix Mendelssohn	230
O lovely peace	George Frideric Handel	112
O praise God in his holiness	Charles Stanford	220
O worship the King	Wolfgang Amadeus Mozart	174
Panis Angelicus (2-part)	César Franck	65
Panis Angelicus (4-part)	César Franck	70
The Lord is my shepherd (SA)	Franz Schubert	140
The Lord is my shepherd (SSAA)	Franz Schubert	150
The Lord is my shepherd (SATB)	Franz Schubert	125
The Lord's my shepherd (Crimond)	Jessie Irvine	215
The Lord's Prayer	Michael Head	118